COUNSELING SUICIDAL PEOPLE

Counseling Suicidal People
A Therapy of Hope

Third Edition

PAUL G. QUINNETT

Spokane, Washington

Third edition 2009. Sixth printing 2017.

The QPR Institute

P.O. Box 2867

Spokane, Washington 99220

(888) 726-7926

Design and typography by A. E. Grey

Cover design by Pamela Larson, Keokee Co., Sandpoint, Idaho

Printed in the United States

Publisher's Cataloging-in-Publication Data

Quinnett, Paul

ISBN 978-0-9705076-1-7

Counseling suicidal people: A therapy of hope / Paul Quinnett

    1. Counseling–suicidal people. 2. Psychology applied. I. Title.

This book is dedicated to all the people who have taught me about suicide in the most difficult and painful ways: those who have lost a loved one to suicide yet have themselves survived, those who have seriously considered suicide yet have never attempted it, those who have attempted suicide yet live on, and those who died by their own hand yet left the gift of their stories behind.

CONTENTS

PREFACE

IN 2004, suicide accounted for more than 32,000 deaths in the United States, making it the eleventh leading cause of death (American Association of Suicidology 2007). If it is challenging to imagine what this number means, it translates into one suicide approximately every sixteen minutes, or more than 89 people per day. But this is only the tip of the iceberg. For every death by suicide, there are roughly twenty-five attempts, and among young people the rate of attempted suicide is higher still. For every young person who dies by suicide, anywhere from one to two hundred others will make a nonfatal suicide attempt, sometimes resulting in serious physical injury (Goldsmith et al. 2002). Hospitalizations for serious self-injury exceed 150,000 each year.

Another vast chunk of the iceberg likewise remains hidden. In any twelve-month period, literally millions of people in America think seriously about suicide (Goldsmith et al. 2002). In a study conducted among high-school students in 2005, 16.9 percent reported that they had seriously considered attempting suicide within the past twelve months, and 8 percent actually made one or more attempts during the same period (Eaton et al. 2006).

As such statistics suggest, anyone who works in the field of mental health encounters suicidal people. The question is not *whether* we will meet suicidal people but how well prepared we will be to help them when we do. Research has confirmed that, above all, it is the accurate diagnosis and aggressive treatment of underlying psychiatric disorders that helps to prevent suicidal behavior. Having worked with hundreds of suicidal patients over almost four decades of practice, and having kept up with the literature on the relationship of suicide to mental illness, I am certain of one thing: Treatment saves lives.

I am also certain of another thing. Not every suicidal person will seek treatment, and, of those who do seek help, not all will accept it when they find it. Nor will the appropriate treatment necessarily be made available to them. An elderly, retired white male will be diagnosed with a sleep disturbance, but his primary depression will remain undetected. A suicidal alcoholic who was a victim of physical and sexual abuse in early childhood will be arrested on a drunk driving charge, prosecuted, and directed to an alcohol recovery program. But the post-traumatic stress syndrome with co-occurring depressive disorder from which she now suffers will go undiagnosed and untreated. An angry young black man with a history of irritable and aggressive behavior will be jailed for petty robbery, but his bipolar mood disorder will be ignored. Preconceptions, carelessness, complacency, expediency, poorly conceived approaches to mental health problems, simple ignorance—all can lead to errors that could have been avoided and thus to needless tragedies.

If mental illness carries a stigma, being mentally ill and suicidal carries a double stigma. Too many people suffering from psychiatric illnesses have died by suicide without ever realizing they were sick. The love of friends and family and the imagined protection of above-average intelligence, a superior education, and worldly success are no protection against the agony of a tormented mind tantalized by the perceived relief that suicide promises.

Suicide is extremely complex—perhaps the most complex

of all human behavior. Counterinstinctive, impossible to predict in the individual case, suicide has historically been surrounded by fear, accusation, and inadequate scientific understanding.

But things are changing.

Since the first edition of this book appeared, in 1992, and especially since the *Surgeon General's Call to Action to Prevent Suicide* was issued in July 1999, suicide prevention has moved forward. Leadership has emerged, and the National Strategy for Suicide Prevention has outlined a public health approach to the problem of suicide. Sources of funding have opened up, and implementation has begun. Statewide plans have been developed and brought to life. Colleges and universities have become involved in efforts to deter suicide, as have law enforcement agencies, leaders of Native American tribes, the military, and emergency services personnel. Two new national crisis lines are operational: 1-800-SUICIDE and 1-800-273-TALK. All across America, suicide prevention programs are up and running.

In addition, people who have lost a relative or close friend to suicide have chosen to take action. Survivors of suicide have joined groups, founded organizations, rallied their communities, sewn quilts, petitioned Congress, and helped pass legislation. Their efforts have contributed to a growing public awareness not only that suicide devastates millions of lives each year but that suicides can be prevented. The public is beginning to realize that:

- ◆ Suicidal behavior is not rare: Suicidal thoughts, feelings, and actions are clearly within the experience of millions of people.
- ◆ Suicidal behavior can and does result in disability and/or disfigurement, as well as in premature death.
- ◆ Suicidal behavior comes at great cost to any soci-

ety, not only in the form of direct expenditures for medical and psychiatric care but also in emotional anguish and bereavement.

◆ The psychiatric illnesses that are considered the necessary preconditions for the vast majority of suicidal thoughts and feelings are increasingly treatable, and recovery is a reality.

In short, suicide is no longer the taboo subject it once was but has become instead an issue of practical importance—to ordinary citizens and, in particular, to those of us in the helping professions.

As the public comes to understand the connection between untreated psychiatric disorders and suicide and to recognize that suicide can be prevented, greater expectations for quality care will be directed at professionals who work with persons at risk. Those of us in the helping professions must be prepared to respond in an informed and effective fashion. What we were *not* taught as students about the detection, assessment, management, and treatment of suicidal persons will become apparent if a suicidal loved one dies in our care, and we will be held accountable. In fact, it is already happening: Alleged negligence in cases of suicide is reportedly the leading cause of malpractice suits filed against mental health professionals (Slovenko 2002, 779). Unless we acquire greater skill in working with suicidal people, our credibility as healers will be diminished—and, more important, lives will continue to be unnecessarily lost to suicide.

Fortunately, we understand much more about suicidal behavior and its causes than we did even ten years ago. We are not without resources. Research is expanding our knowledge, and therapeutic approaches grounded in solid scientific evidence have been developed and are constantly being refined. Each of us already possesses a powerful medicine: the lifesaving skills of understanding, empathy, and caring, the ability to listen and to guide, and the desire to give hope to the hopeless. Each of us can learn something of value that will help suicidal people. There is reason to hope that our successes will more and more outnumber our defeats.

This book is devoted to what we as practitioners can bring to the healing environment that is established when one human being offers help to another. The ideas and recommendations to follow are based both on the current scientific literature and on experience gained in my career in the fields of clinical suicidology, substance abuse, suicide prevention, and psychotherapy. My perspective is personal as well as professional, and what I have to say should certainly not be construed as the last word on the subject of suicide intervention and treatment. Detailed information regarding these topics is available in many of the sources provided in the list of references.

For information to be helpful, it must be clear and comprehensible. With a view to enabling a broad base of practitioners to make good use of what we know, I've done my best to write in language unencumbered by professional jargon. And in response to the many requests of my students over the years, I have tried to focus on concrete, practical interventions, ones that I have found to work.

If this is your first step along the road to understanding suicide, I encourage you to continue your journey.

Anyone who willingly enters into the pain of a stranger is truly a remarkable person.

—HENRI J. M. NOUWEN—

COUNSELING SUICIDAL PEOPLE

INTRODUCTION: ENCOUNTERING SUICIDE

I WILL NEVER FORGET the first suicidal person I encountered. I was a young graduate student in psychology working in a state mental hospital when a logger was admitted. He had a nasty chest wound where he had attempted to run a hunting knife through his ribs and into his heart. I listened to his long story of woe. He had lost his job, his wife had left him, and he had started drinking again. His pickup had been repossessed and, on a spree in a bar, he had gotten into a fistfight in which two of his teeth were knocked out. Drunk and despairing, he stumbled out into the snow, unsheathed the knife he carried on his hip, and tried to kill himself. As his tale drew to a close, I remember thinking, "My God! This man needs professional help!"

But, of course, I *was* the professional, no matter how green I might be. My chief therapeutic success with my first seriously suicidal patient was to avoid bolting from the room in panic. Perhaps like you, I had received no training in suicide risk assessment and was essentially clueless about what to say or do.

Now, forty years later, I rarely panic. In fact, over the past many years I have worked almost exclusively with suicidal people. Colleagues often refer patients to me, and, because of my reputation in the community, suicidal people themselves seek me out, as do their family members and friends. I'm glad they do, and I am grateful for what they have taught me and for the opportunity to share some of that knowledge with you.

I confess that, as a graduate student, I was something of a maverick. Try as I might, I could not find a theoretical approach or "school of therapy" in which to place my total faith. An incorrigible eclectic, I admired everything from the behavioral methods of B. F. Skinner to Carl Jung's theories about symbolism to the pragmatism of Albert Ellis to the caring approach of Carl Rogers.

But then I went to graduate school well before some of the more compelling studies on the efficacy of specific psychotherapies had been published. Given the weight of evidence that has since accumulated for the effectiveness of cognitive-behavioral therapy in the treatment of depressive disorder and, in particular, suicidal thoughts and behavior (Brown et al. 2005), I now view this approach as the one most likely to achieve positive psychotherapeutic outcomes, and I believe it should be our first line of defense. However, the issue at stake—life or death—pushes one to embrace existential and dynamic therapies as well. And, late at night, when no one is around, I sometimes read sociobiology and evolutionary psychology, as it seems that much of the explanation of human behavior lies in our genes and in the environments in which we evolved.

That said, I have generally been more interested in *doing* things that worked than in understanding *why* they worked. And so I was always disappointed that my professors couldn't give me more guidance about exactly what one should say or do in the counseling session. At times, this led me to wonder whether they really knew what to say or do, especially with suicidal patients.

My goal here, then, is to provide you with specific things to say and do. What I wish to pass along are tools that have worked for me, in hopes that some of them will work for you. Where these ideas and techniques for intervention are supported by research, I have provided references to some of the more important studies.

The Language of Suicide

When people talk about suicide, the language they use varies. It differs according to age, sex, and level of education, as well as with cultural and ethnic background. In mainstream America, a culture still largely dominated by white males, a speaker can choose from any number of slang terms to describe suicide: "I feel like offing myself," or "I think I'll take a dirt bath," or "I'm going to eat my gun." In contrast, a young Native American might speak of planning to "take the spirit trail." An eight-year-old may not know the word *suicide*, but even a child will understand what it means to say, "I want to get in front of a truck." For many teenage girls in our culture, taking an overdose and then just drifting off is such a common suicidal fantasy that it has come to be known as the "Sleeping Beauty Plan." Anyone who wishes to be an effective counselor of suicidal people will need to be familiar with this vocabulary. Be aware that people use euphemisms when they are frightened or embarrassed by a subject. Despite a shift in public attitudes, many people are uncomfortable talking openly about suicide, and so they turn to slang to express their suicidal intent or desire.

Broadly speaking, the risk of suicide increases with age. Those working with older people must therefore be especially sensitive to suicidal language—and, especially, to its absence under conditions in which any seriously depressed person might consider suicide a reasonable alternative to his or her present circumstances. Elderly people are often reluctant to talk about suicidal thoughts and feelings, which means that the counselor must be more direct and inquiring.

Indeed, it is frank talk about suicidal thoughts and feelings—as symptoms of an illness—that makes lifesaving interventions and treatment possible. If professional healers and community gatekeepers hope to play a role in the prevention of self-directed violence, we must learn to talk about suicide. In what follows, I have tried to suggest ways we can establish a therapeutic environment in which both sufferer and healer are at ease. When both parties in the therapeutic relationship can talk openly about a subject as difficult, and as frightening, as suicide, a foundation of hope is laid, and the prospects for genuine psychological healing are enhanced.

I have often thought that working with suicidal people is the equivalent of emergency room trauma surgery. The person in front of you is dying—if not literally, then dying of depression, of despair, of acute and utter hopelessness. Doing therapy with suicidal people is not for the weak of heart, but it can be the most rewarding work imaginable. Learn to speak the language of suicide, and you will begin to save the lives of those who suffer a pain so exquisite that only death seems a remedy.

The Suicide Journey

Suicide is a process, not a fixed event. Simply put, this means that when you first come into contact with someone who is contemplating suicide, you could be meeting that person at either end of what I call the suicide journey.

The suicide journey begins with the idea that killing oneself will end suffering—that death will solve the problems and pain of living. The journey ends, sometimes, with a completed act of suicide. Except for highly impulsive persons (and suicidal people can be impulsive), the majority of suicidal persons are on roughly the same journey. The back roads, the stretches of highway, and the detours may vary, but all those who ultimately kill themselves must begin with the thought of suicide, however fleeting, then move on to active contemplation of the idea, and eventually formulate what they believe will be a fatal plan.

As suicidal people move closer and closer to the tragic conclusion of their journey, they usually send signals to others that they are nearing the end. These signals will vary from silent behavioral clues, to verbal threats, direct and indirect, to suicidal gestures, to nonfatal suicide attempts. One way or another, though, before taking the final action, a suicidal person generally communicates his or her intention to die to others.

The journey to suicide can be a short, swift one, but it is more likely to be long and labored. Where you meet someone along this tortured road has important implications for the journey's outcome. If, for example, you happen to be the first person to become aware of the passive suicidal thoughts of a never-before-suicidal young person who is currently facing problems that seem overwhelming, your chances for success should be fairly good. If instead you encounter a man in his late fifties whose career has failed and who is under indictment for tax evasion, who has a severe drinking problem, and who has twice been divorced and has just learned that his third wife is leaving him, you may be meeting someone whose journey toward suicide is nearly at its end.

The way we respond to each of these travelers is critical to helping them survive. How best to greet these travelers— what questions to ask and what actions to take to keep them safe—is the stuff of the first part of this book. In it, I deal with intervention and the assessment of risk, and with risk management.

The second part of the book is directed at therapists, counselors, clinicians, and others who work with suicidal people. As such, this section looks at the many ways we can use our human capacities and individual talents, our training, and the healing relationships that we have established to help weary travelers not only pass over a stretch of bad road but learn to enjoy the journey of life as far as its natural end. Often cast in the form of strategies and techniques, these are the tools from which you may pick and choose in your work with suicidal patients.

Finally, I share some thoughts about how we as healers can continue to be effective in the lifesaving work we do. I have also appended a page on which you can list the phone numbers of local mental health agencies and mental health providers, including those who specialize in the treatment of suicidal individuals, as well as any other resources that can provide you with a personal support network. Once you have identified the resources available in your community and have made the choices you prefer, you may find it useful to carry the relevant phone numbers with you at all times.

This book is not a comprehensive treatise on the treatment of suicidal persons. It doesn't even come close. But for many who have never studied suicide it will be a beginning. My aim is to translate research into practice and to make what is known about assisting suicidal people accessible to everyone who works with them: crisis volunteers, counselors, pastors, social workers, fire and police chaplains, case managers, youth workers, therapists, physicians, nurses, alcohol and drug counselors, and anyone else in the field of human services.

I call what follows a therapy of hope. I have always believed that it is better by far to be optimistic and miss the mark by overshooting it than to be pessimistic and miss the mark by never trying. As individual practitioners, our job is not to save all of the approximately thirty thousand Americans who will die by suicide this year, much less the estimated one million people around the world who will die by their own hand. Rather, our job is to do our best to save the life of the person in our care. If each of us helps just one soul survive a suicide crisis and recover from depression and despair, we will have done our work well.

If nothing so memorializes our human capacity for misery as suicide, then nothing so rewards our human capacity for compassion as preventing it.

PART I
Intervention

CHAPTER I
Intervention: When It Is Easy

LET'S SUPPOSE THAT YOU HAVE JUST made contact with someone who is either openly suicidal or could be entertaining thoughts of suicide. You immediately know two things: (1) the situation may be serious, or it may not, and (2) either way, you need to do something. The first rule of suicide intervention is *do something!*

Don't stop to worry about doing something wrong. It's doing nothing that gets people killed. Bear in mind that the suicidal, or possibly suicidal, person with whom you're dealing is still with us, so at least part of him or her wants to live. Trust me on this: The part that wants to live is more forgiving of our missteps as interventionists and therapists than you might imagine. So go ahead. Take the first steps.

Six Lifesaving Steps

In an initial interview with a person who may be suicidal, you will need to accomplish a number of basic goals, which are outlined below. But before you embark on a full-scale crisis intervention, you'll first have to decide whether the person in your office is suicidal.

1. THE S QUESTION

If the question "Is this person possibly suicidal?" has already entered your mind, it is reasonably likely that thoughts of suicide are already in the mind of the person you're worried about. But you can't be certain—so just *ask*.

Cut the tension and ask:

"You look pretty upset. Are you having any thoughts of
    death or suicide?"
"Have you been thinking about ending your life?"
"Have you ever wanted to stop living?"
"Do you ever wish you could go to sleep and never wake up?"

If the person has hinted at suicide—saying something
like, "I'd just like to get life over with," for instance—go
ahead and confront him or her with an explicit question:
"Do you mean you're thinking of killing yourself?" Or,
"Have you been thinking of suicide?"

There are any number of ways to ask about suicidal
thoughts and feelings, and, in the face of a real situation,
you may come up with ones that suit you better than any of
these. But here is how *not* to ask the question: "You're not
thinking of suicide, are you?" Framing the question in this
way encourages a negative reply—it suggests you want a "no"
answer, not a "yes" one—and so it closes the door on the
suicidal person. It says, in effect: "Please don't burden me
with your troubles." Other than that, any question that
goes right to the heart of the matter will work.

However, not unlike asking about another S subject—
sex—asking about suicide can be difficult. I have trained
thousands of clinicians over the years, and one of the most
common complaints I have heard about raising the question of suicide is that "the words seem to stick in my
throat." But the words *should* stick in your throat: You're
asking someone whether he or she wants to die. It's hard to
imagine a more emotionally charged question.

You may also find yourself thinking, "What if I find out
that this person really *is* suicidal? What do I do then?" Or
you may wonder, "Am I going to put the idea in this person's head by asking? What if I make things worse?" It is

okay to worry about what will happen next, but try to limit your worry to less than thirty seconds. In particular, do *not* worry that asking the S question will foster suicidal thoughts. Research has shown that talking about suicide does not increase suicidal thinking or behavior (Gould et al. 2005). On the contrary, asking about suicide can, and does, save lives.

Stop worrying, then, and just ask the question. If you don't ask, the person you're trying to help may conclude that you can't even bring yourself to talk about what they're thinking of doing to themselves. And if you, a professional, can't talk about suicide, then who can? If you're not sure you'll be able to ask the S question when the time comes, practice it with a colleague.

Asking whether someone has recurrent thoughts of death or suicide should become a routine and comfortable habit. It should, in fact, be part of your standard workup. If such inquiries are not a matter of routine, many suicidal people will escape detection on their initial interview. For thirty years, I was the director of a large clinical service at Spokane Mental Health, where asking incoming patients about suicide was mandatory for all clinical staff. At intake, close to half—46 percent—of those admitted to outpatient programs evidenced suicidal thoughts or feelings and/or proved to have a recent history of attempted suicide.

The fact remains, though, that routine questioning about suicidal thoughts and feelings is not the current standard of care for many in the helping professions, apart from psychiatrists. Among other things, lack of specific training in suicide risk detection and assessment discourages such questioning. As a physician once put it to me: "What am I supposed to do if they say 'yes'?" Another objected: "If they say 'yes,' there goes my schedule for the day! Now I've got to stop and listen. I've got a waiting room full of people, you know." In other words, those who are seriously depressed cannot count on their doctor—or even a mental health professional—to inquire about recurrent thoughts of death or suicide.

Understandably, we are all at least somewhat reluctant to talk about a subject as upsetting as suicide. And yet suicidal thoughts and feelings are often the most important indication that someone is suffering from a serious, but treatable, clinical depression or a substance abuse disorder (or, as is often the case, both) that has so far escaped notice. Until the S question becomes the standard of care in all health-care settings, we will continue to miss opportunities to prevent suicide.

When you first conduct an interview with someone you suspect may be suicidal, you should try to ask the S question no later than twenty minutes into the session. That way, if you get a "yes," you will have enough time to conduct a more in-depth assessment and develop collaborative crisis and risk management plans. After all, if the answer to the question is "yes," you must take that answer seriously. It is extremely unwise to disregard suicidal thoughts or feelings, nor should their importance ever be minimized. I once saw a young man in my office who had gone to an emergency room only a week before complaining of insomnia, overwhelming depression, and constant thoughts of self-destruction. He had recently suffered terrible losses and, with a history of clinical depression dating back to childhood, coupled with substance abuse, he was now in a suicidal crisis. At the hospital, he had been seen by a psychiatrist who had explained to him that he was "not all that suicidal" and had prescribed a thirty-day supply of an antidepressant. Three days later the young man locked the door of his apartment, took all the remaining medication, and tied a plastic bag over his head. Fortunately, he didn't die.

If you ask the S question and get a "yes," then, as a professional, you are obligated to take reasonable and responsible action to prevent a suicide attempt. And this means you must also be prepared to share the sufferer's pain. We humans are social creatures. We depend on each other and are stronger for it. If you ask me whether I am thinking about killing myself, then it must be that you have noticed my pain and care enough about me to ask. And if you care about me that much, then surely I must care about you enough to talk about my pain. If I admit to you that I am thinking about suicide (because you asked), I am no longer as alone as I thought I was. You have broken through my isolation, and, in a positive sense, I owe you. Asking the S question—being willing to begin a conversation about life and death—means that we are in this together.

Provided it is not worded so as to encourage a negative reply, the S question works a certain magic. In its best outcome, asking the question produces an immediate sense of relief in the suicidal person. The result can be the beginning of a lifesaving intervention.

Some years ago I conducted a small study of patients presenting to our mental health center with thoughts of suicide. Each underwent a structured clinical interview regarding their suicidal thoughts and feelings, their plans for suicide, and their past history of thoughts or attempts. Patients who saw their clinician as comfortable and competent when it came to asking questions about suicidal thoughts and actions reported higher levels of hope about the future than did patients who did not share this perception (Quinnett 1998).

Finally, don't be afraid to ask the S question because you think it is somehow intrusive. It's the unasked questions that lead to tragedy. Threats of suicide are often coded in some way, appearing as hints that can sometimes be difficult to interpret. Under such circumstances, it is better to be bold and blunt than shy and sorry. And, after all, if you ask the question and discover that your patient is *not* suicidal, that's good news.

2. ASSESSING IMMEDIATE RISK

Once you know that the person you're talking to is indeed feeling suicidal, the question becomes, How suicidal? I will have more to say about assessment later in the chapter. But at this point in the intervention it is important to get answers to a couple of basic, and closely related, questions. First, is this person determined to die right away, or can his or her suicide attempt be put on hold? And, second, is the person willing to talk?

If the answer to the second question is yes, we can talk, then there's no need to push the panic button. In fact, people who have just been asked whether they're feeling suicidal are usually quite willing to talk. Most of them have wanted to talk to someone for weeks, or months, or years. This is why, if you've just learned that someone is suicidal, it's a good idea to make at least an hour available to begin the listening process.

As a first step in assessment, you will need to determine whether the person in your office has ingested any medications or other chemicals that could prove fatal. If you have reason to believe the person you're dealing with has taken an overdose or is in any other way in physical danger, call 911 or 211 and request a paramedic or emergency medical service unit. Folks who overdose often haven't a clue about how much of what kind of medication or poison or combination thereof they have taken. Unless you are properly trained to assess possible medical emergencies, let the folks who are take over.

Remember, though, that the great majority of suicidal people we encounter are not in the throes of an actual suicidal attempt, nor are they planning to kill themselves within the next ten minutes. Maybe tomorrow, or next Friday, or by the end of the month, but not right now. Acutely suicidal people—those who are in a high state of arousal and agitation as they approach some final act of self-violence—are rarely seen outside of emergency rooms or psychiatric hospitals, or at the physical location they have selected to make a suicide attempt, or occasionally in hostage situations. Moreover, imminent-risk-for-suicide episodes typically last only a short while, at most a few hours. Emergency department staff see such patients, as do police, firefighters, paramedics, and acute-care mental health professionals.

In the case of suicidal people who are not in imminent danger, the desire to die may be relatively strong or weak, and it is unlikely that you will know at the outset just how at risk someone is. If you are in doubt about the answer, ask more questions. In multiple studies (Beck, Brown, and Steer 1997; Joiner, Rudd, and Rajab 1997, Joiner et al. 2003), suicidal desire has been demonstrated to consist of the following basic elements: the absence of reasons for living, the wish to die, the wish not to carry on, passive suicide attempts (example, not eating, or not taking needed medications), and the wish to make a suicide attempt. Other researchers have suggested that feeling trapped, feeling hopeless and/or helpless, and feeling intolerably alone also contribute to suicidal desire (Rudd et al. 2006; Williams et al. 2006; Baumeister and Leary 1995). So do severe psychological pain (Shneidman 1998) and the belief that one is a burden on others (Joiner 2005).

The open expression of suicidal desire might thus include statements that the person is thinking about suicide or sees no reason to go on living or feels trapped and hopeless, and so on. Asking questions about these states of mind will help you to determine the intensity of the person's desire for death. For example, you can ask, "On a ten-point scale, how hopeless do you feel about the future?" Or, "Do you feel you are a burden on someone else?" Or, Can you tell me how you're going to find your way out of this mess?" Only by drawing the person out will you be able to establish the level of comfort you need with a patient in order to continue to be helpful. One way or another, though, your immediate goal is to determine how urgently the person in front of you wishes to die.

It may be that your job description doesn't include working out an answer to this challenging question. If you are in the detection and referral business, for instance, your task is simply to identify the fact that some degree of suicide risk is present and then to arrange for someone with the necessary training and experience to conduct a risk assessment interview and determine the best course of action and the plan for treatment. Otherwise, and especially if you are a professional with medical and/or legal responsibility for the services you render, you may wish to consider formal training in suicide risk assessment.

3. BUILDING RAPPORT

Even though you may ultimately be going to refer the suicidal person to someone else for longer-term care, if the work of intervention is to be productive, you must establish some degree of rapport with the person in your office. Among other things, you need to find out what the suicidal person believes that suicide would accomplish. You can begin simply by asking the suicidal person to describe the situation he or she is facing. When the person falls silent, ask more questions:

> "It sounds like you may lose the house. Where would this
> leave your family?"
> "From what you're saying, it doesn't seem like there's
> much hope she'll come back. What do you think?"
> "If you fail this course, does it mean your parents won't
> let you go on to college?"

Remember that the world's oldest safe assumption is "Assume nothing!" The more questions you ask, the more answers you'll have, and the more you'll understand. And the more the suicidal person believes that you really do understand, the better things will go.

Here are several suggestions that will help you win the trust of someone who is suicidal:

- Pay perfect attention. "What people really need," Mary Lou Casey once said, "is a good listening to." Good rapport is nothing more than paying such close attention to people that, afterward, they report that *you paid attention to them.*

- Unless the person is manic and is rambling on and on or is intoxicated or psychotic or otherwise incoherent, don't butt in. Say to yourself, "Listen . . . listen . . . *learn.*"

- Remain calm, and be willing to talk about suicide openly, as if this was something you did every day.

- The suicidal person is desperate to find someone who is warm, competent, and collected—someone who doesn't frighten easily and isn't put off by talk of suicide. You're it.

- Don't condemn the idea of suicide, but don't praise it either. Accept it as an interesting option but possibly too much solution to whatever problems are at hand.

- Normalize feelings, especially feelings of panic and the sense of being overwhelmed. Saying something like, "I think anyone in your situation would be pretty frightened"—that is, helping a suicidal person recognize that whatever emotions he or she is experiencing are to be expected under the circumstances—generally has a calming effect.

- State plainly that you plan to be there to help the person through whatever mess he or she is in. Just say it: "I'm here. I'll help you through this."

- If you feel platitudes like "I understand what you're going through" or "You'll feel better in the morning" or any other bumper-sticker slogan about to roll off your tongue—bite it! Platitudes don't play well with people who are experiencing severe psychological pain. If the easy stuff worked, suicidal people wouldn't be suicidal.
- Don't be afraid to say that you don't understand.
- Because you are talking to a suicidal person, you can assume, right off, that they don't feel as if anyone understands. So never say you *do* understand unless you're sure you really do. And the only way you can be sure is to have that understanding confirmed by the suicidal person.

What most encourages suicidal people to share their innermost thoughts and their emotional pain is a compassionate human response to their description of suffering. Expressing a solid faith in a positive outcome also helps. But this optimism cannot be Pollyannaish or simpleminded. If the sufferer's problems were easily solved, chances are they would have already been solved.

The main message you need to convey to a suicidal person during your first meeting is this: "Yes, the situation is desperate, but it is not hopeless. Something can be done, and something will be done!" You can cement this good-faith offer with the assurance that "No matter how rough things get, we're going to get through this together." If this produces even a weak smile or a small sigh of relief—to say nothing of an agreement to put off what seemed inevitable only minutes or hours before—then you can consider your mission well on the way to being accomplished.

4. CREATING A SAFE ENVIRONMENT
Once the suicidal person has agreed to wait and talk, we

also need to work on ensuring the person's immediate safety. You have already taken a step in this direction by establishing that no medical emergency exists. But creating a safe environment also means removing any means to self-harm the person may be carrying or have at home. To do so, you will need to ask whether the person has any knives, razors, guns, or pills in his or her immediate possession. Then, if the person is holding onto such materials, you will need to persuade him or her to relinquish them.

If you are talking to a man standing on the ledge of a ten-story building who says he intends to jump, getting him inside to talk is the first step toward a safe environment. So is convincing someone to hand over a stash of pills or put a gun down on your desk so that it can be put away somewhere. (Suicidal people are typically not homicidal toward those trying to help them. But accidents can happen—so if you're not familiar with firearms, it is best not to pick a gun up yourself.) If the means to suicide are at home, it is essential that the suicidal person agree to their disposal. If the client is a child or an adolescent, a responsible adult must be enlisted to make the home safe.

The timing of this step is up to you, but it is generally wise not to embark on it at the very start of the interview. Convincing someone who is overwhelmed with despair to relinquish the means to suicide can be difficult. After all, you are asking that person to give up what may very well seem like the one remaining avenue of escape. And so don't be surprised if a suicidal person is reluctant to hand over the means to suicide right off the bat. It may be that a safe environment cannot be achieved until you have established a degree of rapport with the suicidal person and have the beginnings of a relationship of trust.

If you are simply not able to obtain a commitment to safety from someone who is suicidal, then you will need to consider inpatient hospitalization. This is a topic I will discuss in the following chapter. But securing someone's consent to be safe is worth whatever effort it entails. Keep in mind that if you show yourself prepared to leave an agitated, anxious, hopeless person in possession of the means to suicide, the suicidal person could interpret this as a lack of concern ("If my therapist really cared, she wouldn't have let me keep my pills").

Telephone counseling is especially challenging. If your best efforts to convince someone to make a commitment to safety and future treatment fail to produce that promise, you must up the ante. When the person on the phone cannot or will not agree to be safe, and you feel the risk is high, start a trace and initiate rescue procedures. Send in the police, paramedics, or a mental health crisis team. You obviously can't reach down a phone line and take away a gun, nor can you determine (with any reliability) how many pills someone may have taken or how recently. If you are in any doubt, reach out.

Yes, there will be those who subsequently complain that you violated their privacy by sending in a third party to assess them against their will. Rest assured, though, that those who threaten to sue almost certainly won't. After all, they called you; you didn't call them. Then, too, they would have to prove to a judge and jury that you harmed them in some way by violating their civil rights, and this will be a hard case to make when you are clearly a good-hearted, well-intentioned human being who was trying to save a life.

In the course of my long career at Spokane Mental Health—which offered outpatient programs, inpatient liaison, emergency services, medication management, and a 24-hour crisis line—we were occasionally threatened with lawsuits on the grounds that we had violated someone's civil rights. All these threatened lawsuits—including those stemming from an intervention that resulted in an involuntary psychiatric hospitalization—evaporated into thin air after the person got treatment and began to feel better. Besides, in the end, I would rather have a patient angry with me for a few days than dead forever. So don't let a fear of lawsuits stop you from summoning help when you feel it is needed.

5. EXTENDING THE SAFETY NET

Now relax. You're doing fine. You're not even an hour into this, and already you can see glimmers of hope. The suicidal person has agreed to stick around long enough to see what can be done. You've laid the foundations of a life-saving relationship. Now, in the breathing space you've established, you need to start widening the safety net. You can approach this task from two angles.

You can start by *gathering additional information from the person who is at risk*. This means continuing to ask questions. It means delving into the person's life to learn all you can about what is driving the present crisis. Is there a family history of suicide and/or of mood disorders, substance abuse, domestic violence, or other known contributors to suicide risk? Is there a role model for suicide? What has pushed the suicidal person to the very verge of a suicide attempt? Was there a trigger of some sort? Other than putting an end to emotional pain, is there anything else the person thinks that suicide would accomplish? Again, there is safety in knowledge. The more complete and nuanced your understanding of the person and the situation, the better able you will be to offer effective help.

In addition, you can *get others involved.* Others may be your colleagues or your supervisor, or they may be psychologists or psychiatrists able to offer second opinions and useful advice. If the suicidal person has family in the area, give careful consideration to letting them know that one of their loved ones is contemplating self-destruction. In particular, parents of young people need to know when their child is in trouble. In some states, the law requires the disclosure of such matters by, for example, school personnel when a child is under a certain age.

The decision to notify other people will also depend on the laws governing confidentiality and on your employer's own rules about disclosure. In addition, the suicidal person's wishes should be taken into account. Sometimes a person wants to die in order to hurt someone else. If this appears to be the case, make certain that contacting this "someone else" won't make the problem worse. However, under no circumstances should you promise to keep a suicidal person's status a secret. To be drawn into such an agreement puts you both at risk.

To get others involved, ask the suicidal person whom he or she would like to have informed about the crisis. Simply say: "Who else needs to know you are in this much pain?" Then ask permission to get in touch with the person or persons. Although this is not likely to take place during the initial interview, once the network of communication has been expanded and the needed permissions obtained, you will be able to learn more about the suicidal person's situation from friends, loved ones, or family members.

I cannot overemphasize the importance of information known to the family but not to you. For whatever reason, the suicidal person may well minimize his or her suicidal status to you, but family members may be more forthcoming—and their observations often prove critical in assessing risk. At your first opportunity, then, you should make every effort to learn all you can, not only from family members but from anyone else who knows the person well, including the person's doctor.

6. CRISIS MANAGEMENT

As a final step in saving a life, unless the person in your care is being admitted to the hospital, you will also need to set up a crisis management plan. It is best to keep such a plan simple. An effective crisis management plan consists of three basic elements: safety, phone access, and clear instructions about what to do if the going gets rough.

Safety. The best way to manage a crisis is to try to prevent it from ever developing. And so, as we have seen, you need to ensure that the suicidal person will be safe once he or she returns home. This means arranging for someone who genuinely cares about the person to be immediately available, preferably under the same roof. It also means that someone responsible has removed all the means to suicide, such as guns or pills, from the place of residence. Remember that, especially among the young, suicide is sometimes an impulsive act. By removing temptation, a safety plan frustrates suicidal behavior. It also sends a very important message: *We don't want you to kill yourself!*

Phone access. Everyone knows 911 or 211, but many people are reluctant to use these numbers—so don't assume they will. Instead, give both the suicidal person and the person who is going to be part of the survival plan at least three telephone numbers: (1) 1-800-SUICIDE or 1-800-273-TALK and/or the number of a local crisis line; (2) the number of a hospital emergency department where immediate medical care is available; and (3) your office number, as well as any backup number that may be appropriate. It's up to you whether to give out your home number or cell phone number. The more personal the connection, the better, however. You've already built a lifesaving bridge to the suicidal person. Now the person needs to know that the bridge will still be there once he or she leaves your office, and that it is open and easy to cross.

Crisis instructions. Give clear instructions to the suicidal person and to his or her friend, parent, or caregiver about what to do should a crisis appear to be developing. In particular, make sure that someone knows for certain how to get from crisis to solution—how to get to the nearest hospital or mental health crisis team in an emergency, for instance. Murphy's Law—if things can go wrong, they will—seems to operate overtime with suicidal people. So, again, assume nothing.

Once a plan for immediate crisis management is in place, you will still need to persuade the suicidal person to commit to continuing treatment. This future care may come from you, or it may be that you will refer the person to someone else. If so, you will naturally want to make the best possible referral you can under the circumstances—but what counts most is that the suicidal person not walk out your door without a follow-up appointment. Make sure you've done at least the following:

- Write down the name and phone number of the therapist or doctor the suicidal person will see next, along with the date, time, and location of the appointment, and give this information to the person presently in your care.
- Set the referral up while the suicidal person is still with you. If possible, he or she should be given the opportunity to speak directly to the therapist or doctor on your phone. Confirm the next appointment among the three of you.

As a safety net, this human connection is everything. If you feel the person you've been working with is resistant to following through with the referral, you can plan to take the person to the appointment yourself or arrange for some significant other to do so. But before making such arrangements, you would do well to reevaluate the situation. It could be that you've underestimated how bad things really are and that hospitalization would be the more sensible course of action.

Risk Management

Whether you are going to treat or counsel a suicidal patient yourself or refer the person to someone else, the relative success of your efforts to secure an honest, good-faith commitment to future care is an important test of how willing the person is to give life another try. People are unpredictable. They can be desperately suicidal, and yet, given a chance to commit to treatment that will help them stay alive, they'll take it. Other people, whose suicidal feelings appear to be of roughly equivalent strength, will *not* make such a commitment.

That said, the outcome of an intervention—whether the interview ends with the patient recommitted to life or still resolved to die—very often depends on the relationship between the sufferer and healer. There can be little doubt that the quality of the rapport that has been established influences the quality of the data collected and, therefore, the quality of the assessment and the intervention. My experience both with suicidal people and with those who evaluate and treat them strongly suggests that interviewers who are perceived as aloof and uncaring, or perhaps even subtly hostile, can actually enhance the risk of suicide. Interviewers who are seen as friendly, open, warm, and sincere are the ones who contribute most to reducing that risk. Of course, we can never be certain how we are coming across to another person—but we *can* do our best to convey our honest concern and our desire to help and to create a genuine sense of connection.

It is generally best to hold off on asking someone to make a safety agreement and participate in a risk management plan until you are convinced that the person trusts you. Unless the sufferer believes that you are genuinely on his or her side, your efforts to secure a commitment to safety may meet with little success. Then again, after an hour or so of working with someone, you may feel so confident about how things are going that asking the person for a specific agreement to stay alive seems unnecessary. My advice, however, is to ask for a recommitment to life anyway—if only to be sure you haven't misread the person. That way, if the worst happens, at least you'll have the comfort of knowing you left no stone unturned.

A full-fledged risk management plan involves much more than the promise to stay alive, however. It involves informing the suicidal person of the benefits and the potential drawbacks of a proposed approach to treatment (possibly including a referral) and then collaborating in an action plan designed to reduce risk factors and increase protective factors. As part of this action plan the suicidal person also commits to remaining safe and following medical advice so that the work of healing—counseling, a program of medication, family therapy—can begin.

As research has shown, a large proportion of people who kill themselves are under the influence of alcohol at the time they die (Murphy and Wetzel 1990; Foster 2001; Bertolote et al. 2004). To take one example: A study conducted in 2004 that examined the toxicological profiles of suicide victims in thirteen different states revealed that alcohol was a contributing factor in 33.3 percent of the deaths. Drugs were also implicated: 16.4 percent of the victims tested positive for opiates, 9.4 percent for cocaine, 7.7 percent for marijuana, and 3.9 percent for amphetamines (Karch, Crosby, and Simon 2006). Because alcohol and other mood-altering substances play such a major role in suicide, it is critical that the suicidal person agree not to drink or use drugs until treatment is under way. Although the immediate psychological effects of alcohol in the bloodstream are to some extent unpredictable, alcohol distorts our judgment. It also clouds our ability to imagine the consequences of our acts, including suicidal ones. If we're depressed and/or angry, alcohol may provide short-term relief, but the effects of intoxication on our mood can seriously impair our ability to think clearly and to make sound decisions. This impaired judgment, coupled with the increased impulsivity that alcohol can produce, means that highly lethal situations may develop very quickly.

If you suspect that a suicidal person has been drinking or is under the influence of drugs, ask. Moreover, never assume that someone who's had something to drink is sober just because he or she says so—and be aware that no one under the influence of alcohol or drugs can make a good-faith commitment to anything, let alone a recommitment to life. If the person is unable or unwilling to make a commitment to safety by agreeing to abstain from alcohol and drugs until treatment is in progress, a more vigorous intervention may be necessary, including a formal assessment for substance abuse. My clinical experience has convinced me that recovery programs for alcoholism and addiction, including Alcoholics Anonymous, are among our most powerful tools in the suicide prevention movement.

A safety agreement can be a simple verbal understanding. Your conversation with the suicidal person may culminate with something like, "Will you give me your word not to kill yourself until we've had a chance to sort these problems out?" Or, "If we're going to work together, I need you to agree to stay alive. Will you do that?" Suicidal people who are highly distraught and/or intoxicated, or who appear to be suffering from acute mental illness, are in no condition to make promises. Otherwise, for the vast majority of suicidal people, their word is their bond—and if you can get the verbal promise sealed with a handshake, so much the better.

Alternatively, a safety agreement can involve a signature. A written agreement is not unlike the informed consent that patients sign when they agree to a surgical procedure. The patient is presumed to be legally competent and to have the capacity to understand and appreciate both the benefits and the risks of the treatment proposed. I will have more to say about no-suicide contracts in the following section. For now, let me just say that I've never been one who thought much of written agreements between us and the people who need us. A formal contract tends to suggest that we don't trust each other and ought to have lawyers involved. So I'll take a handshake and smile every time.

The patient's medical record will record a great deal more information than is covered in the suicidal person's agreement with you, however, especially concerning the elements of the proposed plan for safety and future treatment. Your employer (hospital, clinic, counseling center, etc.) may have a written statement outlining what patients can, in general, expect by way of a standard of care, such as certified staff and the provision of a safe environment. Typically, though, such statements do not specifically mention measures designed to prevent suicide. In fact, the matter of patient safety as regards suicidal behavior has only recently been formally targeted as a goal by the Joint Commission on Accreditation of Healthcare Organizations (Joint Commission 2007).

No matter what else you say—or don't say—to the suicidal patient, you will always be expected to deliver the standard of care for your community. After all, at the very least the patient has a right to competent and ethical service. Beyond that, however, many things are possible—and only you can determine what you are personally willing and unwilling to put on the line for a given suicidal patient. Some therapists won't take calls after business hours; others will. Some agree to make house calls; others refuse. You must decide for yourself what you are prepared to include in your offer of treatment—your half of the bargain, whether explicit or implied. Whatever you do, though, don't bet the patient's life on a promise *you* can't keep.

Any intervention that ends with a person who was actively suicidal only a short while before agreeing to remain safe and to pursue treatment has achieved its purpose. Hope, however tenuous, has been revived. Thanks to you, the suicidal person may be ready to step forward into the future.

When More Is Needed

In most cases, suicidal people will agree to hold off on their plans for suicide without putting up much of an argument. They'll shake your hand and promise to wait and talk. Having found a sympathetic listener, they already feel some measure of relief. In some cases, though, suicidal individuals may be suffering from a serious psychiatric disorder or may be so emotionally distraught and/or intoxicated that asking them to make a commitment to safety is simply not reasonable. Some will outright refuse to consent to a safety agreement, while others will be evasive or will promise to stay alive only for the next twenty-four hours, or for three days, or for a week.

If a suicidal person is willing to postpone suicide for, say, a month, you have some cause for hope. But if you can't persuade someone to agree to a few hours, a day, or a week, or if you're unable to elicit any sort of good-faith promise from the person to remain alive long enough to see a referral plan through and begin treatment, then you have a problem. In all likelihood, you are dealing with someone who is so deeply mired in despair that what he or she is really saying is, "Thanks for listening, but I'm still going to kill myself."

If so, then you will need to consider a more aggressive course of action.

CHAPTER 2
Intervention: When It Is Hard

THE LAST CHAPTER FOCUSED on suicidal people who were probably only just beginning the journey toward self-destruction. They may have been entertaining the notion that death might be preferable to life, or they may have been temporarily convinced that it would be, but they were not yet overwhelmingly invested in dying. No matter what the risk factors stacked against them—age, sex, race, alcohol abuse, clinical depression—they were, at least for the time being, willing to consider the idea of sticking around to see how the rest of life might turn out. To pursue our traveler's analogy, they could agree to keep on living long enough to discover whether the stretch of bumpy road they'd been traveling was perhaps only a short section under construction on the way to a smooth highway not too far ahead.

To put it another way, these people didn't so much want to die as to end their suffering, and so persuading them to commit to safety and treatment was relatively easy. Where hope is readily restored by a single intervention—by a healing act of kindness and compassion—the risk of suicide diminishes rapidly. So rapidly, in fact, that beyond checking from time to time to make sure a subsequent problem hasn't triggered fresh suicidal thoughts, you can generally lay those worries aside. Once treatment is under way and the person has begun to feel better, life's problems start to seem more manageable. As a result, the idea of suicide can quickly lose its appeal.

Sometimes, though, interventions don't go so well. The person you're talking with is headed into what he or she sees as the last mile of life and isn't willing to give up suicide as a solution. The person may be facing so many different problems—acute, lifelong, or both—that it appears there is no way out. You have worked as hard as you can for an hour or more, but the sufferer remains unconvinced that there is any reason for hope to be revived.

And why should the person trust you? For someone who is overwhelmed with despair, making a leap of faith is difficult. And, after all, you may have only just met. For all the person knows, you're merely some do-gooder who has never known and cannot possibly understand real psychological pain. And yet here you are, asking for the sacrifice of the only solution that promises real relief.

When Someone Is Unwilling to Accept Help

As we have seen, a suicidal person who is intoxicated or so severely agitated as to be out of control is in no condition to ensure his or her own safety. But, although it may seem strange to say, under most circumstances the only person who can ultimately reduce the risk of suicide is the suicidal person. To put it another way, people who are truly determined to kill themselves will probably find a way to do so, sometimes even in the security of a psychiatric unit while they are under a close suicide watch. In attempting to safeguard someone's life, we therefore need help from that person in the form of his or her cooperation. This is one reason why the quality of the relationship we have with the suicidal person is so important. When the person is unable or unwilling to cooperate, however, our best bet is to rely on the power of treatment in the safest environments we can create.

As a rule, people who have invested a good deal of time, effort, and sometimes money in a plan for killing themselves will not let it go without a struggle. They may not have figured out how to live, but they may very well have determined how best to die. In fact, coming up with a plan for suicide may have given them the only real sense of personal control and accomplishment they've recently known. They may thus feel that, in seeking to keep them alive, you are trying to take way their power—that you want to rob them of this one promise of relief. And so they resist your help, which may also seem to them too little too late. When asked for a commitment to safety and treatment, some take evasive maneuvers. For example:

- They can't remember where they put the gun.
- They want to keep the stash of pills "just for a little while longer."
- Sure, they'll agree to see you the next day, but they're not making any promises after that.
- "Don't worry about me," they tell you, "I won't bother you when the time comes."
- "Thanks," they may say, "you've been real helpful. Until now I wasn't sure what to do. But I feel much better after talking to you. Can I go now?"

When you start hearing this sort of thing, and you begin to feel uneasy, you should. You can figure the suicidal person is thinking something like this:

- "You seem like a nice person, but I've trusted people like you in the past, and look at what a mess my life is."
- "I don't know whether the help you're offering will put a stop to my suffering, but I'm sure the gun I have in my purse will."
- "Thanks for trying, but you don't really understand me. Now I'll just have to go ahead with my plans."

If a suicidal person refuses to give you a clear, good-faith commitment to safety and to the future, you have more work to do—and you're facing a tough situation. What you do next is probably going to make the situation seem worse. I say "worse" because what you do next will probably run counter to the wishes of the suicidal person and leave him or her even more upset, as well as angry. However, you've come this far, and there's no other way out. After all, you now know that something is terribly wrong, and you are morally bound to try to do something that will help make whatever is wrong right. You are in a life-and-death crisis with the suicidal person.

It is at this point that the healer usually realizes that he or she cannot safeguard the suicidal person's life all alone. Additional support is needed. There may be no choice but to consider the safety of a psychiatric hospital, a hospital emergency department, or some other secure place. Under such circumstances, you simply must move ahead. But forcing the issue will surely test any small alliance with the patient that you've managed to establish.

Known Risk Factors

No matter how obvious a suicide may seem after the fact, predicting suicide is impossible. The laws of probability tell us how likely or unlikely it is that a particular type of event will occur, be it a plane crash, an earthquake, or the suicide of an individual. But they cannot give us specifics. We know there will be plane crashes, but which plane and when? Similarly, those of us who work with suicidal people, and are familiar with the profiles of high-risk individuals, know that many older, white, alcoholic males in the throes of depression will kill themselves. But we cannot say precisely which ones, under what circumstances, and on which days.

In the United States, the base rate for suicide is approximately 12 deaths by suicide per 100,000 persons per year

(American Association of Suicidology 2007). In other words, the number of suicides is very small—so small that our chances of making an accurate prediction are almost nil. If you were asked to wager whether a given person will die by suicide, your best bet would be to say no. And in most cases you would win your bet. Typically, then, "predicting" suicide is a matter of 20-20 hindsight—"I knew he was going to do it; all the signs were there." But even warning signs don't enable us to make accurate predictions. Thousands of suicidal people send warning signs, but only a few complete a suicidal act.

The Surgeon General's Call to Action to Prevent Suicide, 1999 (U.S. Public Health Service 1999) lists the following as major factors in the risk for suicide:

A previous suicide attempt (or attempts)
Psychiatric illness—particularly mood disorders such as
    depression and bipolar disorder
Co-occurring mental and substance abuse disorders
A family history of suicide
A sense of hopelessness
Impulsive and/or aggressive tendencies
Isolation, a feeling of being cut off from other people
A recent loss, whether personal, social, financial, or
    job-related
Physical illness
Easy access to lethal materials, especially guns
Poor access to mental health treatment
A reluctance to seek help because of the stigma attached
    to mental and substance abuse disorders and/or to
    the idea of suicide
The influence of significant people—friends, family
    members, celebrities—who have died by suicide,
    whether this influence is exerted through direct
    personal contact or coverage in the media

Some cultural and religious beliefs—for instance, the
belief that suicide is a noble way to resolve a personal
crisis
Local epidemics of suicide that have a contagious influence.

The list of risk factors could go on and on. But the risk
of suicide cannot be adequately assessed simply by adding
up risk factors. Likewise, data from psychological tests or
personality inventories leave too many questions about the
current level of risk unanswered.

Risk factors can include stable variables—age, psychiatric
illness, past attempts at suicide, a history of divorce—as well
as unstable ones, such as agitation, lack of sleep, or intoxication. But suicide generally occurs in a swirl of the above,
and most often in a psychosocial context over which we have
very little control—a circumstance that considerably com-
plicates risk management. A statistically vulnerable person
may be at a relatively low risk for suicide one week but at a
relatively high risk just a few weeks later. Similarly, we may
judge a teenaged girl who is terribly upset because she has
just been jilted by her boyfriend to be at a statistically lower
risk of taking her life than a seriously depressed, narcissis-
tic, alcoholic sixty-year-old man who is equipped with a
gun, bullets, and a specific plan to end his suffering. But
that does not mean the girl will live and the man will die.
Just the opposite could happen. Despite our best efforts at
prediction, clinical experience has proven, again and
again, just how wrong we can be.

But if we can't predict suicide, we can take all reasonable
precautions to prevent suicide, especially once we know a
person is thinking about taking his or her own life. We can
familiarize ourselves with the known risk factors and make
efforts to reduce them. We can also educate suicidal people
and their families about the factors that increase the risk of
suicide, thereby providing them with information that

could help them manage that risk. We do this for people at high risk for cardiac illness, diabetes, and cancer. So why not do it for people who are at risk of suicide?

In addition, we can gather information about protective factors and do what we can to enhance them. Although the notion of protective factors—buffers against suicide—is perhaps less familiar than that of risk factors, enhancing protective factors plays a crucial role in reducing the risk of suicide. It is well known that even acutely suicidal people are ultimately ambivalent about dying. The will to live has not altogether vanished. Preserving that part of them that wants to stay alive are the sustaining beliefs and core values the person holds most dear, as well as a fundamental sense that there must be some purpose to life. Good health, close friends, religious convictions, a sense of responsibility to others, especially children—factors such as these give a suicidal person reasons for living. In particular, the existence of a network of social supports helps to shield suicidal people from actual suicide attempts (Joiner 2005); so does the existence of plans for the future (Strosahl, Chiles, and Linehan 1992). Yet another buffer is engagement with someone who is trying to provide the suicidal person with alternatives to death—someone who represents life-affirming ideas and options. Once someone is in treatment, the person's relationship to his or her therapist may therefore provide an additional protective factor, as can the person's willingness to adhere to a medication regimen, to eat a good diet, and to get plenty of rest.

When it comes to assessing how at risk someone is, gaining insight into protective factors is at least as important as evaluating risk factors. A person thinking of suicide who can quickly list ten reasons why he or she should go on living is probably not on the very verge of an act of self-destruction. More often than not, though, when suicidal people are asked to name reasons why they might want to continue living, they are unable to come up with more than a very few. A thorough clinical interview—one that elicits both risk factors and protective factors—offers the most effective means to deter a planned suicide, especially when the protective factors, however initially slim, can be marshaled to support life.

Above all, in conducting an assessment, we need to forget about trying to be omniscient. We must remain humble and proceed on the basis of what we actually know, rather than cling to preconceptions. We must be able to answer the question, "How do I know what I know?" Even though we may do so unwittingly, it is dangerous to rely on myths, on antiquated ideas, or on possible prejudice. Especially when it comes to directing a suicidal person into a more restricted environment, such as a psychiatric hospital, we need to have asked enough questions to make an informed judgment—however imperfect that judgment may prove to be. No matter what methods you use, how skillful you are, or how many times you have seen similar suicidal people and been led to the same conclusion, your judgment will be always just that, a judgment. The more you have learned about someone, however, the more reliable your judgment is likely to be.

Making the Decision to Hospitalize

Hospitalizing someone who is at risk of suicide is not always the best thing to do. But under some circumstances it is. Making this call is one of the most delicate, and most important, tasks that mental health practitioners are paid to do. However well or poorly they do it, their actions are always based on facts and judgments derived from the risk assessment interview.

If we think about a suicidal person's journey toward self-destruction as a process with a beginning, a middle, and an end, then by the time such a person can no longer be persuaded to make a commitment to safety and treatment, he or she is well down the road to an actual suicide attempt, and possibly death. A suicidal individual who cannot or will not accept help is automatically at high risk. In the language of the law, he or she now presents a "danger to self." If a person appears to be out of control and/or if you judge that person to be unable to make a firm and considered promise to remain safe and pursue treatment, then hospitalization is generally the best choice. In fact, if you cannot secure a good-faith commitment to safety, you have little choice but to recommend hospitalization, or at least to get other people involved who can help you make this decision. Failing the suicidal person's willingness or ability to consent to a safety agreement, to dispose of the means of suicide, and otherwise to cooperate in his or her own future well-being, few choices remain.

Almost always one or more symptoms of severe depression, serious or global insomnia, raging anxiety, alcohol or drug intoxication, a psychotic disorder, or other signs of acute psychiatric illness will accompany the acute suicidal state. Therefore, although arriving at the decision to recommend hospitalization can be difficult, justifying that decision generally is not, although you will need to be prepared with convincing information regarding the suicidal person's status. Whether or not the hospital will be able to admit the person is another matter, but if the interview data and reports by third parties clearly indicate that someone is a danger to self "by reason of a mental illness," hospitalization is understood to be the safest course of action.

If you are not yourself a mental health professional, it is not your job to decide whether admission to a hospital is indicated. There are, unfortunately, continuing problems with suicide risk assessment—what it should be and how best to standardize it. These problems include questions concerning the proper standard of care (Simon and Shuman

2006). If in doubt, and especially if no psychiatrist or psychologist is immediately available to give you a second opinion on your assessment, step outside the intervention relationship momentarily and make some calls. In such circumstances, you need support from others. You certainly don't want to steer someone away from a hospital if that's where the person belongs.

Confronted with the prospect of going to the hospital, whether voluntarily or involuntarily, many suicidal people will suddenly try to convince you that they aren't really all that suicidal or begin explaining why hospitalization just isn't feasible. They'll say things like:

"But I'll be all right. Honest I will!"
"I was only kidding. I'm not going to kill myself."
"Oh, come on! Why are you taking all this so seriously?"
"Mental hospital? Do I look crazy to you? I'm not going to any mental hospital."
"*Hospital?* I can't go to a hospital! Who will look after my cat?"
"I'm already broke. I can't afford to go to a hospital."

Having decided to recommend hospitalization, you should expect some anger from the suicidal person. After all, you're restricting—or threatening to restrict—this person's freedom. Some may get downright nasty and start swearing at you, while still others may threaten to sue.

These reactions are unfortunate but unavoidable. But once you have made up your mind that the suicidal person you're working with is not safe and needs a supervised and secure environment, you can't afford to give in to the person's anger. If, down deep, you believe that this person is at serious risk and is struggling to break free from the safety net you are constructing, you cannot back away from your decision. In fact, if you back off from your decision at this juncture, a suicidal person could interpret your reversal as evidence that you've changed your mind about whether the future holds any promise. The suicidal person might conclude, "Ha! I was right! There *is* no hope."

Emotional Involvement

At this point in any difficult suicide risk assessment interview, strong feelings are bound to come up on both sides. The suicidal person came in upset and is probably even more upset by the suggestion that he or she cannot be trusted to manage his or her own life.

The person's autonomy is in jeopardy. He or she may claim that his or her constitutional rights are being infringed and argue that this is a free country and you can't force people into confinement. The person's hostility can be very genuine, and you too will be feeling some strong emotions.

The good feelings of empathy and understanding you had toward the suicidal person only moments before may be replaced with boredom, impatience, anger, fear, or frustration. In my experience, such negative reactions to a suicidal person are an important source of information. They tell you that the sufferer is attempting to drive away or alienate the very person who could be of help. It is as if the person is saying, "Get away from me! Can't you see I'm already dead?"

So, when you are working with suicidal people, it is a good idea to monitor your emotional reactions to them.

Boredom, impatience. Feeling suddenly bored with a suicidal person's problems may signal that you have sensed, probably unconsciously, impending defeat and so are withdrawing emotionally from the relationship. You've devoted all this time and energy to someone, and now the person doesn't want to cooperate and follow your guidance. You're tired, it's late and, after all, there are better things to do than to keep spinning your wheels with someone who can't seem to understand that what you're proposing is for the best.

Anger, fear. It is very possible that you will feel angry. If someone places his or her life in your hands and then tries to tie your hands behind your back, becoming angry is an understandable reaction. Anger is usually caused by fear. When you're trying to save a life, the fear comes from the feeling that you're failing. Here you've been trying so hard to help, and now you're being told to get lost—that your efforts haven't been effective. You may also have the sense that you're being backed into a corner. Given that the person currently in your care won't agree to hospitalization and yet is at serious risk, you have only two alternatives: Give in to the person's objections, which might result in a suicide, or resort to an involuntary admission, which means calling in the law. The thought of having to choose between two not-very-appealing options may make you angry, but it can also produce fear.

Frustration. Even if you do suicide assessments for a living, expect to feel frustrated. Someone's life is at stake. The person is now less than cooperative and is testing all your skills. Without necessarily meaning to, the person may be pushing you to the limits of your kindness, and your patience. This is okay. Consider that a lot of people may have let this person down lately. As he or she sees it, you just happen to be the next one in line.

Knowing that these emotions are to be expected may help you identify them as they occur. Being aware of such emotions is good, not bad. It means that you're on top of things, that you know what's going on inside you. Depending on the circumstances, it might be a good thing to share your reactions with the suicidal person. For instance, you might say, "You know, I'm getting a little frightened here. We've been talking together for a while, and we'd gotten started on sorting out some of your problems. But now you're acting like you don't want me to help you anymore. Have you had this reaction with other people you've talked to?"

The answer you get to this question could prove quite valuable. Very often a suicidal person will have had other, similar conversations in the past, conversations that were ultimately unhelpful. Your question could cut right to the heart of the matter and so help put your relationship with the suicidal person back on track. In addition, acknowledging that you share the suicidal person's sense of fear and impotence can have an equalizing effect, making you seem more like a human being and less like a figure of authority who is trying to force the suicidal person to agree to confinement.

Another potentially useful approach is to say something like: "I realize you may not be able to make a commitment to safety and treatment right now. That may be okay for you, but it isn't okay for me. I'm here to do the best job I can to keep you alive, and I intend to do it." When you make it clear that you're determined to make a stand, a suicidal person will often calm down and go along with the program. As he or she will understand, what you're essentially saying is, "Look—I'm the one with the objectivity and good judgment here, and I've decided to pry your fingers from the wheel and take over the driving." You're the designated driver, the clear-thinking and sober one, and you're doing the right thing. More often than not, the suicidal person will return later on and thank you for having had the courage to act in his or her best interests.

Voluntary Hospitalization

In addition to psychiatric units and psychiatric hospitals, any residential treatment center, nursing home, structured group home, or other facility where patients remain overnight can be considered an inpatient setting, at least in terms of the increased responsibility borne by staff once they know that a patient presents some clear and present danger to himself or herself. If a suicidal person will agree, however reluctantly, to enter a hospital voluntarily, this is best. Involuntary hospitalization can get complicated, and it is always tougher on the patient's sense of pride and self-worth.

Voluntary hospitalization should be relatively easy to arrange, provided you have the essential risk information needed to convince the admitting staff of the seriousness of the crisis. But I must warn you that because of the limited number of inpatient beds, admission of a suicidal patient is not guaranteed. In fact, you may have to argue your case at some length to get the person admitted—which is why you need to do a comprehensive interview and have indisputable data at hand.

Meanwhile, your main message to the suicidal person should be that you want him or her to be safe. You want the person to get a good night's rest, to get started on medications, to talk with some doctors and nurses—to put things on hold and stay for a while in a safe place. Suicidal people have been struggling, usually for a long time, to solve their problems and will very often welcome the chance for a little relief—even after a show of initial resistance. They can always save face later on by explaining to their friends, "I didn't want to, but they insisted."

You can ease the transition to a safe environment by knowing a little about modern psychiatric hospitals and sharing what you know with the suicidal person and his or her family. Addressing fears, whether these are imagined or real, is the quickest and most effective way to persuade someone who is seriously suicidal to agree to a voluntary admission to the hospital. Here is some information to help you in your efforts:

- Hospital stays these days are generally short, ranging from a few days to a couple of weeks
- Hospital staff are well trained and understand the suffering that suicidal people experience
- Voluntary patients don't *have* to do everything asked of them—including taking medications
- Similarly, other treatments, including electro-convulsive shock therapy, cannot be given without a patient's permission, even though the treatments are in fact safe and effective
- Hospitals guarantee a patient certain rights, which (though they vary somewhat from state to state) typically include the right to have access to a phone, the right to have visitors, the right to observe religious practices, and the right to confidentiality
- Modern psychiatric hospitals are places of healing that respect the patient's dignity; they are not snake pits or prisons.

Once you have convinced the suicidal person to enter a hospital, your remaining work with the person should be reasonably straightforward. The customary steps to a psychiatric hospitalization are:

1. If you haven't already done so, call a psychiatrist or an emergency room physician who can agree to hospitalize your suicidal person. He or she will need the following information:

   - The person's sex and age; the nature of crisis; whether the person has been drinking or has taken drugs; and what (if any) prescribed medications the person is on.
   - Your diagnostic impressions. Everything you've learned about the person's suicidal thoughts and

feelings, about his or her degree of impulse control, and about any past history of suicide attempts is important.
- The phone number of a family member or significant other.

Some admitting physicians will want more information,
but unless you are yourself a highly trained professional, it
is unlikely they will expect very much. They will need to
know enough to justify an admission, but solid evidence
of the imminent potential for suicide is usually sufficient.

Not all hospitals have psychiatrists on call, and so you
may be told to contact a mental health center. Staff will
take responsibility for screening the person for hospitalization.

2. Anticipate the patient's worries and agree to manage
   arrangements for child care and pets, or to talk to
   employers or apartment managers, or to do whatever else
   might stand between the person and his or her safety.

3. If a responsible adult is not available to take the suicidal
   person to the hospital, arrange transportation. Most
   suicidal people could, in fact, get themselves to the hospital, but why take chances? Just about any adult person
   can drive someone to the hospital. Cabbies do fine. If
   the person is acutely suicidal, however, and wants to die
   right now, do not ask any nonprofessional to assume the
   burden of saving a life. Instead, call 211 or 911 and let the
   emergency response operator arrange for an ambulance
   or a police transport.

4. In the case of young people, have a parent or responsible person available at the time of admission to offer
   support and reassurance and to provide relevant history.

5. For your own peace of mind, have the hospital call you when your referral is safely tucked in bed.

Involuntary Hospitalization

Involuntary hospitalization is a last resort. It is what we are obliged to undertake when someone we have identified as at imminent risk of suicide refuses to cooperate in his or her own welfare. If a seriously suicidal person will not agree to voluntary hospitalization, or at least make a good-faith commitment to an outpatient program or the care of a crisis respite service, then we have no choice but to turn to the law. Although the eventual decision will not be ours to make, we must at least try to ensure the person's safety.

Involuntary commitment laws vary in their specifics, but in one form or another they all address the following question: By reason of a mental illness, does this person represent a threat to his or her own safety? If the answer to this question is yes—according to the clinical findings and professional opinions set forth in the petition to the court— then a court has the power to violate someone's civil rights and commit that person to the care and safety of a facility. These facilities are usually state-run mental hospitals or state-approved psychiatric hospitals or units within general medical hospitals. In the United States, an initial commitment is usually limited to no more than two weeks, unless continuing evidence exists that the person poses a danger to self.

Unless you function in an official capacity and have the right (as well as the appropriate legal protection) to order an involuntary psychiatric admission, you don't need to understand, or even necessarily be familiar with, all the particulars of the involuntary treatment laws operative in your state. But you do need to know how to access the people responsible for taking legal action and when to call them.

The systems that govern involuntary detention and treatment vary from state to state, and sometimes even from county to county. For your own sake—and for the sake of any suicidal person with whom you may come into contact— learn how your system works. Then write down the names and numbers of the appropriate contacts and keep the information somewhere handy. When you can answer the following questions, consider yourself properly schooled for your community:

- Who is responsible for evaluating suicidal persons for possible involuntary commitment where you live? The county sheriff? The local or state police? A mental health center? Whom should you call first?
- What information will you need to have in hand when you call?
- Will the people who conduct these evaluations come to your place of work or to the suicidal person's home? If not, how do you get the suicidal person to them?
- How long may a person be detained in a hospital or other facility before the evaluation must take place?
- How long can any involuntary commitment last? What are the conditions for continuing commitment?
- Will you have to testify against the person you are trying to help in order to secure a detention or involuntary commitment?
- At what age may a youth be detained against his or her will in a treatment facility? Under what circumstances do the parents have to be informed?
- Once involuntarily committed, can someone subsequently arrange to become a voluntary patient?

If you can answer these questions, you should be in good shape if and when you are obliged to call on the power of the law to stop a suicide. If you can't answer these questions, contact your local mental health department and get the answers.

As an alternative to involuntary hospitalization, a few crisis treatment systems will provide on-site evaluation and intervention, referral services, respite services, and a complete community safety net. The good news is that these same people will assume responsibility for the survival plan and its implementation. The bad news is that such a sophisticated mental health delivery system may not be available in your community.

Above all, what you need to remember about involuntary hospitalization is that, in the end, the suicidal person's safety is out of our hands. It is not up to us—mental health professionals, school counselors, therapists, nurses, or any human service worker caught up in a suicide assessment situation—to make the final decision about the appropriate course of action. Only a court can decide to infringe someone's constitutional rights for the sake of that person's safety.

The Burden of Decision Making

When we work with suicidal people, we have to ask ourselves: Where else could we find a greater challenge with a greater potential for reward?

Answer? Nowhere.

The moment you become involved in decisions about a suicidal person's future safety, you have accepted one of life's greatest burdens: to prevent someone from dying.

Personally, I cannot think of a heavier burden. As I once remarked to a staff person after a tough suicide consultation, "If this work wasn't noble, I wouldn't do it." Doctors performing extremely delicate brain surgery have a room full of people to assist them, people who will offer consolation if the operation fails—people who will, if need be, stand up for them in court later on and swear, "Yes, Dr. Smith did everything humanly possible."

It is helpful to remember that, to do our work well, we don't have to be gods. We don't need to possess great wisdom, infallible insight, or perfect judgment. All we have to do is make the best call we can based on what we know at the time. This is why getting the facts is so important. Better information leads to better decision making—and yet far too often we do not have all the facts. Suicidal people hold things back. Families keep secrets. Third parties fail to provide us with critical information in a timely fashion. The methods available to us for suicide risk assessment are far from foolproof. Too frequently, they do not give us what any safety engineer would demand to know before making a decision in which lives could be at stake.

But if our work can seem lonely and difficult, it is also enormously fulfilling. Surgeons save people with lasers and scalpels; we save them with words. Abraham Lincoln suffered from serious depression and considered killing himself many times. He was fortunate in his strong will to live, which helped him through periods of despair. In addition, though, he was shielded from suicide by the love of his family and by the support of his friends and colleagues—and by caring words. In the end, all we can do in this work, as in any other, is care enough to do our best. The comfort is that our best is usually good enough.

PART II
Treatment

CHAPTER 3
Good Management and Good Treatment

FROM THE TITLE OF THIS CHAPTER, and from the direction of this book so far, it may seem I am making an assumption—namely, that all suicidal people suffer from some form of mental or emotional disorder. But I'm not making that assumption.

A rapidly expanding literature on the relationship of mental illness to suicide strongly suggests that 90 percent to 95 percent of those who complete suicide are suffering from some sort of disorder in brain function at the time (Goldsmith et al. 2002). This impaired functioning may be due to changes in neurotransmitter mechanisms secondary to brain dysfunction or insult, major life stressors that interact with genetic vulnerabilities to produce specific psychiatric illnesses, drug and alcohol use or abuse, and/or other physical conditions, including those associated with a primary physical illness, the side effects of medication, or disease processes. Because we know so little about those few apparently mentally healthy individuals who end their lives by suicide, my focus here is necessarily on the vast majority of suicidal people whose self-destructive thoughts, feelings, and actions are the consequence of untreated or undertreated brain disorders.

While this book is not the place to address a complete systems approach to suicide risk reduction in care settings or in community settings, it is important to look at some of the fundamental issues. In a clinical setting, a comprehensive suicide risk assessment entails more than simply asking a patient whether he or she is considering suicide and, if so, why. It also includes a thoughtful examination of questions such as the following:

- Is a psychiatric illness present?
- Is there severe anxiety, and what appears to be its cause?
- Is the person physically ill? Is there a thyroid disorder? An undetected tumor?
- Is this person taking a medication or a combination of medications and/or herbal remedies that could cause these symptoms?
- Is there a sleep disturbance?
- Is there a family history of mood disorders or other mental illnesses, or of alcoholism?
- Is there a history of violence or impulsivity?
- Has there been a past suicide attempt? More than one attempt? Death by suicide of any family member? A role model or classmate who died by suicide?
- Has there been any past psychiatric treatment?
- For what problems, and with what result?

This is not an exhaustive list of the items to be covered in a good workup. But whatever the specific questions that are asked, they must address such factors as personality traits that might predispose someone to suicidal behavior, acute psychological stressors, and the possible presence of a psychiatric illness, including co-occurring disorders, or of a genetic vulnerability to such illness. If a psychiatric illness appears to be present, its severity must also be assessed.

Anyone who suffers from serious, chronic psychiatric illness is at a high lifetime risk for suicide. People with co-occurring disorders are at especially high risk—particularly when the second diagnosis is alcoholism or drug addiction. The good news about suicidal crises is that adverse life events of the sort that can aggravate a preexisting brain disorder and precipitate such a crisis are usually of limited duration. To the degree that symptoms of depression are related to stress-spectrum forces, for example, it is possible that the sufferer will pass through a suicidal crisis without benefit of professional care.

The bad news is that, despite the availability of effective treatments, the majority of people who become suicidal are never diagnosed. The failure to identify and then accurately diagnose an underlying psychiatric illness or addiction or to acknowledge the gravity of such an illness can lead to no treatment, inadequate treatment, or the wrong treatment—all of which can have tragic consequences for both the suicidal person and his or her family.

One of the greatest challenges in suicide prevention, then, is ensuring that those most in need of treatment get the help that could save their lives. The chronically ill must have access to affordable and professional care provided by people skilled in the assessment and subsequent treatment of those at high risk for suicide. When you consider that most people who die by suicide are *not* in treatment at the time of their death, the question must arise: Had they gotten the help they needed, would they be alive? Many of us in the field of suicide prevention believe the answer is yes.

Each of the terms *treatment*, *management*, and *therapy* has a distinct meaning. The management of suicidal patients is not the same thing as the treatment of the disorders out of which suicidal thinking and behavior arise. Good management creates a safe environment and establishes sound procedures for the delivery of appropriate treatments, thereby lowering the risk that a patient will die by suicide—both during treatment and after treatment is delivered. Treatment can include medication, socialization programs, and job training, as well as case management; therapy, or counseling, has to do with how we use ourselves—our brains and our hearts—to help others heal. The cold and officious nurse in Ken Kesey's *One Flew Over the Cuckoo's Nest* may be a good manager, one who is able to deliver appropriate medications on schedule. But she does not provide warm, empathic care. To ensure the best outcome for suicidal patients, we need good therapy as well as good management and good treatment.

Good Management: Outpatient Care

It is difficult (if not impossible) to provide good treatment in the absence of good management. Good suicide risk management begins at the top of a healthcare organization, when leadership establishes a culture of safety. This culture is evident in patient-safety education, staff training, and clear and effective policies and procedures.

Increasingly, most of those who suffer from chronic psychiatric disorders and are at high risk for suicide live in the community rather than in inpatient facilities. If we hope to save lives, we must make sure that these individuals have easy access to long-term, community-based case management services of high quality. These services should include aggressive outreach programs aimed at high-risk groups and persons who might be unlikely to self-refer. For a number of reasons, though, comprehensive service and treatment centers for the mentally ill are often either in short supply or else nonexistent, and those that do exist are often poorly funded. And yet nothing is more likely to save lives than access to first-rate outpatient services delivered by well-trained, culturally sensitive staff working out of a fully funded mental health center. Enlightened, affordable, and accessible systems of care offer what is perhaps the most important ingredient of all: hope.

In a nutshell, good outpatient management means installing a community safety net while ensuring that a patient who is potentially suicidal receives appropriate treatment and therapy. In an outpatient setting, a responsible risk management and treatment plan includes the following elements:

- A network of people who are aware of the person's status and can act quickly and with authority on his or her behalf to provide some modicum of safety. Among others, such a network might include family members, patient advocates, and peer support specialists.
- A clear plan of action in the event of a crisis. This plan should be one that all involved have agreed upon in advance, and all should be familiar with the steps to be taken.
- A prearranged access route to hospitalization, should this become necessary. If at all possible, the name of an admitting psychiatrist should be part of these arrangements.
- The flexibility needed to increase the frequency of appointments, family sessions, and conjoint sessions with spouses or significant others as the need arises.
- A backup therapist who will be readily available to the patient when his or her principal therapist is out of town or otherwise not available, as well as a local crisis number, an on-call number, or the national crisis lines 1-800-SUICIDE and 1-800-273-TALK. A bridge between the patient and safety must exist at all times, and it must be short and wide open.
- A close working relationship among the patient's case manager, therapist, and primary care physician, along with any others involved in the patient's care. Sometimes suicidal patients will

signal their feelings to only one person in the network, and not necessarily to the one best suited to take definitive action.

- A method for ensuring that the patient is adhering to a medication regimen, if one is prescribed. Many suicidal patients store up medications with the intention of overdosing if things don't improve. Because medicines cannot work if they remain in the bottle, someone who is reliable needs to confirm that medications are being taken *as prescribed*. The failure to arrange for such oversight could be interpreted by the patient as a tacit invitation to go ahead and attempt suicide.

- A restriction of access to the means of suicide. This precaution should be carried forward from the assessment session into the ongoing risk management plan. Once the patient has agreed to such safety measures, anyone who can help should be enlisted to remove firearms, ropes, poisons, and other potentially lethal materials from the patient's place of residence. This is usually not difficult, but it is critically important. If there are indications that the patient may be prone to impulsive behavior or is liable to begin drinking, those responsible for securing the home need to be especially diligent and attentive.

In addition, a good outpatient management plan takes into consideration the patient's connections in the community (a religious affiliation, for example, or membership in a local organization) and the commitments he or she may have to others: Duties and responsibilities can serve as buffers against suicide. It also pays attention to any changes in care providers. If it is not clear with whom professional responsibility for the suicidal person's welfare lies, tragedy can result.

Perhaps above all, prompt and courteous follow-up is essential. Suicidal people who have reached out, whether to a referral agency or a clinic or a single practitioner, are not given hope by statements like, "Someone should get back to you by Monday." After an assessment interview or an initial contact with someone who ought to be able to help, suicidal people need to feel that they have made a genuine human connection with a person who cares and who can and will help them save their own life. In the absence of this sense of personal connection, all the work of others can go for nothing.

For many years, with the assistance of several devoted colleagues, I directed a suicide prevention hotline staffed largely by volunteers. Our main training message to the many wonderful people who gave us their time and energy was: "Unconditional caring inspires hope, and hope saves lives."

Good Management: Psychiatric Hospitalization

In case of chronic psychiatric illness, relapses are to be expected. It is important that neither the patient nor the provider interpret an episode of acute illness as a "failure" of some sort. A sound case management and treatment plan should therefore make episodic inpatient hospitalization or entry into crisis respite shelters an effortless matter.

As we saw in our discussion of intervention, determining whether a suicidal patient should be admitted to the hospital is often the first major decision faced by an outpatient professional. When it comes to chronically ill patients who are already receiving treatment, a similar question can arise. Under what circumstances does something need to change? If not now, then when?

This is not always an easy question to answer. Especially because the prospect of hospitalization sometimes aggravates a crisis, the decision to hospitalize should be a shared one. The patient's primary care physician should be consulted, and, if you are part of a treatment or emergency response team, so should others on the team. Provided this seems helpful, family members can be included in the decision, and, as far as it is possible to do so, the suicidal person's wishes should also be respected.

It is often useful to think of hospitalization as a way to *buy time* for the suicidal person—time to think things over, to get some sleep, to allow a crisis to cool down, and to talk about his or her predicament with others so that healing can begin. Hospitals can also be the best place for a suicidal person who is not yet in treatment to receive a comprehensive medical and psychiatric assessment, to begin needed medications, and to make plans for outpatient care.

That said, it is well to remember that rarely does a single episode of psychiatric hospitalization solve the fundamental problem. Hospitalization is not going to prevent the recurrence of a cyclical depression, for example. Rather, long-term attention to stress management, outpatient therapy, and, in all likelihood, a monitored medication regimen are what will restore the sufferer and reduce the risk of suicide over the life span. Hospital stays are short, but the problems of those who are vulnerable to suicidal thinking are long-standing. The race to healing will be won by the tortoise, not the hare, and more often by the outpatient therapist than the inpatient nurse.

It is also wise to remember that no one person or treatment facility or hospital can guarantee perfect safety. Even in the security offered by an inpatient setting, suicides do occur. Patient safety is a major concern among inpatient and residential healthcare organizations and their regulatory agencies (see, for example, Fawcett 1997), and creating the safest possible environment for suicidal people is a collective mission. In 2006, the Joint Commission specified suicide prevention as one of its patient safety goals for 2007, and we have reason to hope that even greater attention will be paid in the future to the issue of inpatient suicides.

Moreover, for some patients, hospitalization could be a poor choice, one that might actually make things worse. For example, where a series of brief hospitalizations has produced no lasting benefit, *not* putting the patient in the hospital might be the best option. However, such a recommendation should be preceded by a careful risk-benefit analysis, preferably one carried out in consultation with other professionals. When someone appears to be seriously suicidal, the decision to forgo hospitalization should always be thoroughly deliberated and documented.

Good Treatment

As I noted above, people suffering from mental disorders account for the overwhelming majority of completed suicides. Each of the major psychiatric diagnostic categories, including schizophrenia, bipolar disorder, major depressive disorder, and alcohol dependence or addiction, presents a different treatment challenge, which in turn has implications for both management and therapy. For the chronically ill, good treatment includes careful diagnosis, complete physical, neurological, and psychological workups, and the use of psychotropic medications.

An unanticipated loss or other personal tragedy, or the recurrence of binge drinking that leads to conflicts in a marriage or other close relationship, or the ordinary and progressive downward spiral of health and happiness that accompanies addictive disorders—all may trigger a suicidal crisis. What those who counsel seriously suicidal people must understand, however, is that, regardless of the precipitating factors, a thorough medical assessment and prescribed medications may mean the difference between life and death.

Replicated research from several countries has, for example, shown that, in comparison to patients suffering from other major psychiatric illnesses, persons who suffer from bipolar, or manic-depressive, disorder have the highest rates of completed suicide. Unless properly treated, one in five manic-depressive people will die by suicide. But as the same research demonstrates, when these patients receive ongoing treatment, especially with lithium carbonate, the likelihood of death by suicide drops dramatically (Tondo and Baldessarini 2003).

Similar studies testing the impact of other medications on suicidal behavior are under way. Our job as healers is to know this literature and to use evidence-based interventions, both pharmacological and psychological, to help those at risk of suicide. We also need to remind both suicidal people and their families that new medicines are constantly being developed, one of which may turn out to work for someone who has not responded to the medications currently available. We are living in an age when the neurosciences are making dramatic contributions to our understanding of mental illnesses and suicidal behavior. We have reason to hope, and we have reason to infect others with hope.

This text is not intended to address all of the treatments for psychiatric disorders currently available. Rather, I wish to emphasize three key issues for those who work with suicidal people. The following observations apply to individuals whose level of symptomatic distress—the intensity of their anguish or anger or despair—and psychiatric disability would be rated as moderate to severe by any competent and conscientious mental health professional.

Counseling is not enough. Modern psychotropic medicines that, when taken as prescribed and in sufficient doses, have been shown to be safe and effective in reducing symptoms of distress and improving brain function must be considered the first line of treatment for seriously suicidal people. Indeed, in such cases, relying on counseling or psychotherapy alone is tantamount to malpractice. This means that a medical consultation with a qualified physician, preferably either a psychiatrist or a psychiatric nurse practitioner, must form part of the treatment plan. Whether the patient will take the medication as directed is another issue, one that pertains to management, but clearly the first step is make sure the medications are prescribed.

Aggressive treatment is always indicated. Seriously suicidal people are often living moment to moment, with the prospect of relief, in the form of death, just around the corner. It is therefore essential, during a suicide crisis, that action be taken immediately to reduce acute manifestations of distress. Insomnia, agitation, anxiety, incessant rumination, irritability, hallucinations, and other such symptoms must be targeted and treated definitively. An overly cautious approach typically results in medications being prescribed in inadequate dosages. Does half a dose produce half a cure? No. Half a dose is more likely to produce a treatment failure. What is worse, half doses can lead patients to believe that medicine won't work, which may in turn increase their sense of hopelessness to lethal levels.

Consider what happens when a promising medication fails to reduce a patient's symptoms because less than a full therapeutic dose was prescribed. If a drug cannot reach a therapeutic level in the blood, the patient will receive no benefit from the treatment and so will continue to suffer. This failure could easily lead the patient to conclude: "Even medicine doesn't work, so nothing can help, and so I might as well get it over with." At least if you are suffering without medications, you can still cling to the hope of a magic pill and, on the strength of that hope alone, endure a bit longer. But once you've tried the magic pill and it fails, the promise is gone, and with it the hope of a cure.

In short, too little medication is often worse than none at all. Postmortem studies of blood toxicology have repeatedly shown that people who had been prescribed antidepressant medications and who went on to die by suicide very often did not have therapeutic levels of the drug in their bloodstream at the time of their death. Similarly, when someone appears to be at high risk for suicide, the professional should not worry about prescribing sleeping pills or minor tranquilizers on a short-term basis on the grounds that the person might become addicted. As one patient put it when I evaluated him following a life-threatening overdose, "Either they give me enough medicine to get to sleep, or I will. Permanently!"

There is no safety without sobriety. Good treatment demands assessment of the role, if any, that alcohol or drugs may be playing in the suicidal person's life and, if need be, appropriate intervention. Intoxication impairs brain function, clouds judgment, and decreases inhibitory controls. To provide state-of-the-art antidepressant medications and supportive counseling while the suicidal person binges on alcohol between therapy sessions is like treating someone for a cold instead of the cancer that will kill him.

In conclusion, there is no substitute for good treatment. Talk therapies, by themselves, are not enough. Self-help books and self-help groups can't do it alone. We need to get suicidal people into treatment—by raising public awareness, breaking down stigma, and making treatment and support services readily available. Until we accomplish this much, we cannot expect to substantially reduce the base rate for suicide in our communities.

No-Suicide Contracts
I firmly believe that a good-faith commitment to life (if not necessarily to a particular healer) can go a long way toward reducing the imminent risk of suicide. As we saw in chapter I, convincing a patient to seek further treatment is

an essential step in the informed consent negotiations that frame healing alliances. I have heard many patients say, after agreeing to a safety and treatment plan, that they feel much relieved—that affirming their desire to stay alive and to find a way to feel better has given them newfound hope.

And yet, having reviewed dozens of suicide cases, and having talked with other experts, I know that apparently well-intentioned patient promises *not* to attempt suicide, including written no-suicide contracts, have preceded many an act of self-destruction. I have read far too many medical records of people who completed suicide while under professional care wherein the provider had written of the last contact: "Denies suicidal ideation, contracts for safety."

In a no-suicide contract we ask patients for a written promise, made in good faith, that they will not attempt suicide. As is the case with verbal safety agreements, if a suicidal patient refuses to sign a no-suicide contract, then we know that our therapeutic alliance is not in place and that, in all likelihood, the person is at greater risk than one who *is* willing to commit to safety.

Like verbal safety agreements, no-suicide contracts have certain limitations. Such contracts cannot responsibly be used with patients who are exhibiting symptoms of acute psychiatric illness or who are experiencing extreme distress, agitation, and anxiety or who are using or abusing intoxicating agents. Nor are no-suicide contracts appropriate for use with patients who have little or no impulse control. As a result, they may be of mixed or limited value with children and adolescents, especially those who are highly impulsive or unusually immature. In addition, certain cultural groups hold written agreements in low esteem.

But if no-suicide contracts must be used with due discrimination, those who favor such contracts argue that they offer a number of advantages. Quite apart from furnishing information about a patient's relative willingness to make a commitment to safety, written agreements:

- can serve to foster or reinforce a therapeutic agreement in which the patient formally consents to seek further treatment
- can create a sense of structure in a crisis situation, thereby reducing anxiety
- can give patients a psychological reason to resist what might otherwise be an overwhelming suicidal impulse, as well as with a specific set of instructions that constitute an alternative response to suicidal urges
- may provide a patient some measure of comfort and relief, as the consequence of making a formal commitment to life
- may appeal to a patient's moral code, according to which a promise must be honored, and/or provide "proof on paper" that the patient is committed to life, not death
- can serve as hard evidence that the therapist has heard and understood the plight of the sufferer.

Some practitioners prefer to make a "no-harm" as opposed to a "no-suicide" contract. Such language perhaps makes sense in the case of someone who may be highly distraught and is engaging in self-injurious behavior, such as cutting, but who is not intending to die. Because a no-harm request is not as specific as a no-suicide request, however, in the case of a patient who genuinely *is* suicidal, such language may appear evasive. A no-harm contract is timid, whereas a no-suicide contract is bold. As one teenage boy I saw early in my career explained to me when I asked him for a no-harm contract: "Get real. I don't intend to *harm* myself, I intend to *kill* myself!"

As critics of the contractual approach to risk management have pointed out, a signature on a contract cannot possibly hope to substitute for a thoughtful and thorough clinical assessment of risk or the work needed to establish a genuine emotional bond between therapist and patient, which is the cornerstone of an effective therapeutic alliance. And yet counselors are sometimes tempted to rely on no-suicide contracts in place of something more difficult and time consuming. A written contract may also serve to provide a therapist with a comforting sense of security. Our culture places great faith in the written word. We assume that if we have it in writing, it must be true. The fact that a patient has signed a no-suicide contract can thus lull a counselor into believing something that is simply not true—that suicidal people are actually going to call for help when they are in the middle of a life-threatening crisis or otherwise keep a promise that they are emotionally unable to keep. I remember once asking a patient of mine whether he would call me if and when he again found himself in that dark tunnel of despair. "You don't know what it's like," he replied. "Once you're in there, you don't think of anything but stopping the pain. Call someone? Forget it."

The popularity of no-suicide contracts probably has something to do with the connotations of the term contract, which suggests that an agreement is legally binding. But a contract is a two-way deal. In legal terms, a contract is a set of mutual promises, a meeting of the minds in which each party gives something to get something. Both minds in this meeting have to be legally competent. That is, they must have sufficient cognitive capacity to be able to understand the nature and consequences of the proposed agreement. A contract is automatically void if either party suffers from a serious "mental illness or defect." Therefore, a no-suicide contract with an eight-year-old is suspect, as is one with someone who shows severe symptoms of a psychiatric disorder.

Moreover, precisely because a contract is a two-way relationship, it imposes an obligation on both parties. In the case of no-suicide contracts, a commonly overlooked question is, "What is it that you, the healer, are offering in trade for the patient's offer?"

Do you agree to take calls at home or on your cell phone? If so, how many? At what hours?

Do you promise to provide treatment to this person forever, whether or not your bill is paid?

Do you agree to be kind, thoughtful, and alert at all times, and never to make a therapeutic blunder? In a word, do you promise to practice your healing art perfectly?

Do you agree always to be there when the suicidal person needs you, no matter when?

Having made these promises to your patient, do you understand that, like any other therapist, you will be held accountable by a court for the standard of care you delivered?

And do you find yourself getting a bit uncomfortable trying to answer these questions? Good! After all, you probably didn't intend to make all these promises. However, even though the contract your patient signs makes no mention of such offers, your patient may believe that promises of this sort are implied. So unless you wish to specify, in writing, all the many possible offers you are *not* making to the fragile, recently suicidal person in your care, you may break your promises without even realizing what you've done.

What happens to the contract if you unwittingly violate your implied promises or if, perhaps for reasons beyond your control, you cannot keep up your end of the bargain? The contract is void, for both you and the suicidal person. Every contract has its terms: I give you this, and you give me that. Any change in the terms of agreement—any deviation from the understanding on which the contract is based—is tantamount to a counteroffer. A counteroffer requires a new contract, one that is subject to approval by the other party. If you, as a healer, somehow fail to abide by your half of the agreement, the contract terminates, and a new one must be negotiated.

One serious problem, then, is that our no-suicide contracts with patients are typically one-sided. The patient gives up a lot while we give up almost nothing: We offer in exchange only what we owe to every other patient we serve. Most of what the therapist or doctor is or is not willing to bring to the table is omitted from consideration, and it is what these contracts do *not* say that is dangerous to the patient.

Too many counselors have given little thought to their end of the bargain, and to the degree that they do not understand what *they* are promising, their patient's promise of safety is only as good as the therapist's first misstep. In other words, if the patient expects you to be a miracle worker, and all you do is pull the occasional rabbit out of a hat, your failure to deliver "as promised" can quickly negate the no-suicide contract and plunge the patient into a crisis.

It is probably too late to scratch the term *no-suicide contract* from our professional lexicon. But if you are going to use the word *contract* with suicidal people, please understand that legal language is very precise. A contract is a two-way street, and if one party in the arrangement fails to live up to what was promised, the contract is void. So never bet your patient's life on a contract you can't keep. And remember, there is no evidence that any signed, witnessed, and legal document ever prevented someone from attempting or completing suicide.

Screening for Specific Disorders

As we have seen, the prompt detection and treatment of underlying psychiatric disorders is critical to preventing suicide. Sometimes making a firm diagnosis is a relatively easy matter. But more often it is not. Your patient's symptoms are likely to suggest certain possibilities, but because the same symptoms can be associated with several different disorders, you may be in doubt as to precisely what is going on. If in doubt, seek consultation or a second opinion.

Screening for specific disorders accomplishes two main things. First, it provides you with an independent assessment of the patient's symptoms and their severity, which you can use to confirm or adjust your diagnosis. Second, it offers you an opportunity to confer with your patient about the diagnosis.

DEPRESSION

Let me say at the outset that I am not fond of using the word *depression* to describe the medical condition—the disordered brain and body chemistry—that produces the array of symptoms that make up the syndrome known as major depressive disorder or clinical depression. Depression seems to me too bland a word to do the descriptive heavy lifting this illness demands. Dr. Kay Redfield Jamison captured the true threat posed by this illness when she said, in a radio interview, "Depression is endlessly wicked in its ability to convince us to do things we would not do if we were well." People need to recognize that depression is a life-threatening condition. If we could devise a name for this condition that conveyed something of its agonies and its potentially fatal impact, our work would be a lot easier, and we would surely save more lives.

Not every depressed person experiences suicidal thoughts and feelings, but the majority of people who experience suicidal thoughts and feelings are depressed.

For that reason, anyone who is suicidal should immediately be screened for depression. Various methods of screening for depression are available, and every counselor should have some of these diagnostic tools in his or her office. Free depression screening is also available on dozens of Web sites, including that of Mental Health America (formerly the National Mental Health Association: www.mentalhealthamerica.net). In general, the higher the score on these instruments, the greater the indication that some sort of antidepressant medication may be in order.

The current standard of care in cases of clinical depression, especially if it is diagnosed as moderate to severe, is to give due consideration to the use of antidepressant medications, which may require arranging for a psychiatric consultation. To fail to consider these medications as a first line of treatment for a seriously suicidal person is to ignore a remedy that any reasonable and prudent practitioner would pursue under similar circumstance and with a similar patient. In fact, modern antidepressants are so important to the treatment of depression that if you apparently never explored the option—if you never explained the risks and benefits of such medications to the patient and/or the patient's family—and your patient subsequently dies by suicide, you could be sued for failing to meet the current standard of care.

I don't mean to frighten you, but you absolutely must understand that these medicines effectively reduce the major symptoms of depression in the majority of patients who take them. The most recent edition of the *Diagnostic and Statistical Manual* lists nine major symptoms of depression, and recurrent thoughts of death or suicide is one of them. The presence of persistent suicidal thoughts and feelings—even in the absence of other clear symptoms of depression or signs of mental illness—is reason enough to consider a psychiatric evaluation for the possible need for psychotropic medications. Do not be overly alarmed by reports of an increased risk for suicide following the implementation of antidepressant therapy. Research suggests that the benefits of such treatment far outweigh the risks (Simon, Savarino, Operskalski, and Wang 2006). All the same, the issue remains controversial, and it is a professional's job to stay abreast of the literature.

A great many antidepressant medications are now available. This book is not the place to discuss them in detail, but two broader points deserve mention. First, the newer SSRIs (selective serotonin reuptake inhibitors) are generally preferred to the older TCAs (tricyclic antidepressants), primarily because the former are seldom dangerous in overdose, whereas the latter can be fatal. That said, the most effective medication for a particular patient may be one of the older antidepressants. This is why only a qualified medical provider should make decisions about which medication to prescribe, following which he or she will monitor the patient's response.

Second, antidepressants work only when taken as prescribed. Far too many patients neglect to take their medication at the times and/or in the doses prescribed. As a result, they derive little, if any, therapeutic benefit from the drug, much as happens when a doctor fails to prescribe a medication in an effective dosage. As we saw earlier, the failure of a drug to provide relief can cause patients to become even more hopeless about their future, thereby increasing the risk for suicidal behavior rather than lowering it. Just like half-measures in medicine, half-hearted participation in treatment on the part of patients is dangerous for everyone concerned. The fact that depressed patients often stop taking their medication as soon as they start to feel better poses an additional problem, as discontinuing medication can precipitate a relapse.

More often than not, depression is a chronic illness. As with any chronic condition, taking good care of oneself over time requires learning as much as possible about the illness and about how to manage one's life in such a way as to minimize the risk of getting sick again. It is your job as a healer to make sure that patients suffering from depression understand how deadly serious this disorder is and to help them come to terms with it and manage its symptoms.

ANXIETY AND PANIC DISORDER

As research—notably that of Dr. Jan Fawcett, one of the nation's leading experts on suicide—has demonstrated, untreated anxiety disorders, panic attacks, and panic disorders are associated with an increased risk of completed suicide, especially when these disorders co-occur with depression. Fawcett and his colleagues have described a number of suicide profiles, two of which are characterized by agitation, recurrent ruminative anxiety, and obsessive worrying (Fawcett et al. 1990). Research further suggests that a careful screening for the presence of anxiety symptoms and recent or remote panic attacks should be a routine step in the assessment of suicide risk and the planning of appropriate treatment (Busch, Fawcett, and Jacobs 2003).

In addition to a thorough patient history and direct observation, the Beck Anxiety Inventory has proved a very helpful and efficient tool in screening for anxiety problems (Beck, Epstein, Brown, and Steer 1988). Even in the absence of specific suicidal thoughts, reports of an inability to sleep and a torturous preoccupation with things a patient believes are inescapable, unfixable, and/or unendurable should alert the counselor that the risk of suicide may be very high.

The prompt and aggressive treatment of anxiety disorders appears to be associated with a decreased risk of suicidal behavior (Fawcett et al. 1990). There are many effective treatments, both psychological and psychopharmacological, for anxiety, panic attacks, and panic disorders, and these are often used in combination. If you are not licensed to prescribe medications, do not hesitate to refer a suicidal patient for psychiatric evaluation with a view to possible pharmacotherapy.

ALCOHOLISM AND DRUG ABUSE

Studies have repeatedly found that alcohol dependence and drug abuse are major contributors to death by suicide. Because therapists typically see a patient only once or twice a week, symptoms of alcoholism or drug abuse may not be apparent to them—and yet alcoholics and addicts are at high risk for suicide. Consequently, it is essential to screen for these problems as part of your initial assessment.

One of the simplest and most reliable methods of screening for alcohol and substance abuse problems are the four CAGEAID questions (Ewing 1984). (The mnemonic "CAGE" refers to key words in each of the questions, which are italicized below, and "AID" stands for "Adapted to Include Drugs.") As the interpretive notes provided in parentheses suggest, these four simple questions are a remarkably effective means of diagnosing alcoholism and addiction.

C: Have you felt you ought to *cut down* on your drinking or drug use? (Normal drinkers feel no need to control their drinking, so a yes answer to this question can only come from someone who is worried that his or her pattern of alcohol or drug use is abnormal.)

A: Have people *annoyed* you by criticizing your drinking or drug use? (Society generally defines substance abuse problems in terms of the inappropriate behavior of those who are intoxicated or high. Anyone who is in trouble with a parent or a significant other over his or her drug or alcohol use will likely answer yes to this question.)

G: Have you felt bad or *guilty* about your drinking or drug use? (Nonpathological users seldom do things while intoxicated that they will later feel guilty about. Abusers and addicts do such things all the time.)

E: Have you ever had a drink or used drugs first thing in the morning, as an *eye-opener*, to steady your nerves or get rid of a hangover, or to get the day started? (A yes answer here means that someone is experiencing fairly severe withdrawal symptoms and so may signal middle- or late-stage alcoholism or addiction.)

Two yes answers to these questions should make you suspect that a substance abuse problem exists. Three yes answers suggests that, with the benefit of some additional probing, a formal diagnosis can very probably be made. With rare exception, four yes answers signals that the person is in need of aggressive treatment for substance abuse.

PSYCHOTIC DISORDERS

As noted earlier, most people who die by suicide are suffering from a psychiatric illness of some sort. The following questions have proved useful in the detection of psychotic symptoms:

Have you ever had trouble with your thoughts?
Have your thoughts ever been so confused that you couldn't keep track of your ideas?
Do you ever feel as if you lose control of your thoughts?
Have your thoughts ever frightened or disturbed you?
Have you ever felt that people were watching you or following you?
Have you ever felt that people wanted to hurt you?
Have your eyes or ears ever played tricks on you?
Have you ever heard a voice when nobody else was with you or seen things that were not actually there?

Positive responses to some or all of these questions clearly indicate the presence of a major mental illness, although the precise diagnosis will vary, since, in addition to schizophrenia, several other psychiatric disorders can produce psychotic symptoms. For example, manic-depressive illness, or bipolar disorder, may manifest itself through the appearance of psychotic symptoms, including severe symptoms of depression or mania or both.

Individuals whose thinking is seriously disordered may be unable to exercise control over suicidal impulses, which places such persons at significant risk. The lifetime risk of suicide for persons with schizophrenia has long been reported to be 10 to 15 percent. However, a recent meta-analysis of multiple studies found that the lifetime risk of dying by suicide for people with chronic schizophrenia is closer to 4.5 percent, with most deaths occurring at the onset of the illness (Palmer, Pankratz, and Bostwick 2005). As we have seen, those who suffer from manic-depressive illness are at an even greater risk for suicide. If you detect psychotic symptoms in a patient, then consultation with or referral to a psychiatrist or qualified nurse practitioner is imperative.

Alternative Remedies

Before you embark on standard approaches to treatment, it is important to learn whether a patient has been pursuing some sort of alternative remedy for his or her symptoms. If so, then the doctor who will be prescribing medication must be informed of this. Many people who have struggled with depression know something about the herbal remedy St. John's wort and about omega-3 fatty acids, and they have probably heard about light therapy (or phototherapy) as well. Even Hippocrates was aware that exposure to sunlight could help to lift a depressed mood.

But how well do such alternative remedies really work? Our evidence is somewhat limited, partly because those who pursue such cures typically do so without benefit of clinical supervision. Moreover, the clinical studies that do exist have yielded mixed results. In particular, with the exception of omega-3 fatty acids, we know almost nothing about whether these treatments effectively target and reduce suicidal thoughts and feelings or discourage suicide planning or lessen the incidence of suicide attempts or completed suicides.

In 2002, researchers conducted a randomized clinical trial in which St. John's wort (*Hypericum perforatum*) was compared to a well-known commercial antidepressant and to a placebo (Hypericum Depression Trial Study Group 2002). The herbal remedy was found to be no more effective than the placebo in reducing symptoms of moderate depression. In contrast, it is at this point fairly well established that phototherapy can reduce the symptoms of depression associated with seasonal affective disorder. More recently, studies have shown that light therapy may also be of value in treating mild to moderate nonseasonal depression. We know nothing, however, about the effect of such therapy on suicidal behavior. All the same, used under clinical supervision, light therapy is unlikely to be harmful. In conjunction with other interventions, it is possible that a trial of light therapy would yield some benefit even to a severely depressed patient.

Similarly, mounting evidence suggests that omega-3 fatty acids—found in flax seeds, ocean fish, and certain nuts—have antidepressant and mood-stabilizing effects. Low blood-plasma concentrations of these essential fatty acids have been correlated with low concentrations of the very neurotransmitters associated with mood. In other words, insufficient quantities of omega-3 fatty acids in our diets may be contributing to the impaired brain functions one finds in depression and other mood disorders. As Joseph Hibbeln, a researcher at the National Institutes of Health, has argued, deficits of these fatty acids may play a role in our high rates of depression and suicide.

A seventeen-year-long study of fish consumption in a sample of 265,000 Japanese adults revealed that the suicide rate among those who regularly consumed large amounts of seafood high in omega-3 fatty acids was 19 percent lower than the rate among the group who ate relatively little of these foods (Hirayama 1990). A study published in *Lancet* found that patients treated with mood-stabilizing drugs plus fish oil supplements high in omega-3 fatty acids had fewer recurrences of depressive episodes than those patients treated with medication alone (Hibbeln 1998; see also Parker et al. 2006). According to yet another study, which appeared in the *American Journal of Psychiatry*, omega-3 treatment may be effective in reducing symptoms of depression in children and could thus provide a much-needed alternative to drugs that have been approved for use only with adults (Nemets et al. 2006).

Although such findings are not conclusive, research into omega-3 fatty acids continues, and it makes good sense to keep up with the results of that research. The Web site of the National Institute of Mental Health is a useful source in this regard. Eating plenty of seafood or taking omega-3 fatty acid dietary supplements can't hurt, and, like light therapy, could provide some added help to a patient who is depressed and feeling suicidal. But, especially in the case of someone who is seriously suicidal, to rely solely on omega-3 treatment (or on light therapy or on herbal remedies) would be a serious mistake.

People often assume that natural treatments for depression, such as herbs or fatty acids, are somehow safer and less toxic than prescription medications—but this is a foolish assumption. Natural does not equate to safe. The fact is that the chemical agents we use to combat depression, bipolar disorder, and psychotic symptoms are powerful in their effect. They're supposed to be. Used ineptly and/or without competent medical supervision, however, any of these agents, whether natural or manufactured, can be dangerous. Consider that lithium carbonate is a naturally occurring salt. And yet it is lethal in overdose. For that matter, drinking ten quarts of water at one sitting is likely to kill you. Just because a product is natural doesn't mean it isn't potentially fatal. It also doesn't mean it works.

Another alternative treatment for depression, although not a natural remedy, is vagus nerve stimulation. In VNS, a small, battery-powered generator, which is surgically implanted, sends electrical impulses to the left vagus nerve. We do not know precisely how VNS works, but it appears to influence certain neurotransmitters, including serotonin and norepinephrine, that play a role in depression. First approved for use in the treatment of epilepsy, in 2005 VNS was approved by the FDA as an adjunct treatment for depression. Nonetheless, the evidence in support of VNS as a treatment option is far from conclusive. And, again, we do not know whether such treatment has any significant impact on suicidal behavior.

Am I saying, then, that we should essentially rule out alternative therapies? No. But before recommending alternative remedies, we should first consider conservative, proven approaches to the treatment of mental disorders. We might make an exception if a patient absolutely refuses to take prescription medications, or if the patient has been prescribed effective doses of well-known antidepressant medications, has taken them as directed, and has failed to receive any benefit. As a general rule, though, we should always recommend what we know works best—and this is doubly true when it comes to serious disorders of mood. Dramatic and powerful studies exist, for example, to support the use of lithium in the treatment of bipolar disorder, among them studies that demonstrate its effectiveness in reducing the incidence of suicide. Compared to that, we have almost no evidence to justify the use of other remedies. As one of the finest psychiatrists I've had the privilege to work with once told me, "We work with these medicines every day, all day long. Just about everyone we see is at high risk for suicide. It's what we do for a living, and while it's not exactly like treating the common cold, it's pretty close."

So, if you are not yourself licensed to prescribe medications, make sure your suicidal patient gets competent medical treatment for any serious mood or thought disorder. Psychiatrists do this best. It's their specialty.

Let me also add that, even as I write these words, new evidence-based treatments are being developed, and further breakthroughs can be expected from the neurosciences. Research, including research that focuses on suicide, is ongoing, and much of it is on a fast track. Powerful new drugs that are safe to use dot the horizon. What constitutes effective treatment today will be outdated a decade from now, and perhaps a lot sooner than that. Hope does spring eternal, not only in the human breast, but also in the laboratories of dedicated scientists around the world.

CHAPTER 4
A Therapy of Hope

THE RESEARCH IS IN. Suicide prevention is a therapy of hope. Regardless of how one goes about measuring it in a clinical setting, a sense of hopelessness has repeatedly been shown not only to be a core characteristic of depressed people but also to be strongly associated with other psychiatric disorders that can give rise to suicidal thoughts, feelings, and actions.

As the seminal work of Aaron Beck and his colleagues demonstrated, intense feelings of hopelessness are an important signal of a long-term risk for suicide—perhaps *the* most important. In one study, Beck and his colleagues carried out a detailed psychological assessment of 207 patients who had been hospitalized for suicidal ideation but had no recent history of actual suicide attempts (Beck, Steer, Kovacs, and Garrison 1985). A follow-up conducted five to ten years later revealed that fourteen of these patients eventually died by suicide. As was apparent from a review of the initial data, most of these patients had originally scored 10 or more on the Beck Hopelessness Scale, making it the most reliable indication of an ongoing risk for suicide, followed by high scores for pessimism on the Beck Depression Inventory.

Research has also shown that the intensity of suicidal intent is more highly correlated with hopelessness than with the diagnosis of depression. In a study of 384 patients who had been hospitalized following a suicide attempt, feelings of hopelessness accounted for 76 percent of the association between depression and suicidal intent (Beck, Kovacs, and Weissman 1975; see also Beck et al. 1990). Hopelessness is also a strong predictor of suicidal intent among drug addicts and alcoholics who are suffering from depression (Beck, Steer, and McElroy 1982).

The belief that all is hopeless appears to derive from the impaired cognitive functioning and disordered neuro-chemistry of the depressed mind. In comparison to men-tally healthy individuals, depressed people, and especially suicidal ones, think more slowly and are more constricted in their thinking, are more easily distracted, and have more trouble solving problems (Williams, Barnhofer, Crane, and Beck 2005). People who are struggling with depression cannot project themselves into a rosy future. They are quick to draw negative conclusions and, to make matters worse, suffer from the tendency to recall only failures and other unpleasant experiences, while ignoring positive events, including personal triumphs.

Cognitive-Behavioral Therapy

No one knows for certain precisely how therapy ought to be done with suicidal people. But research on the relative value of specific therapeutic approaches has been under way for some time. As a result, we now have a much clearer understanding of how we should proceed.

As I mentioned at the outset, evidence strongly supports the use of cognitive-behavioral therapy with suicidal people (see, for instance, Brown et al. 2005). Cognitive-behav-ioral therapy focuses on a patient's attitudes and beliefs and, especially, on how the patient interprets his or her experiences. Although healing is fundamentally a gentle process, cognitive-behavioral therapy is confrontational in nature, and the healer's role is often quite directive. The sufferer's beliefs are viewed as hypotheses, not as realities or "givens." Just because someone has concluded that a situation is hopeless, for example, doesn't necessarily mean it is hopeless. It only means that the person *thinks* it's hopeless.

In a nutshell, the goal of the cognitive-behavioral approach is to change the way a patient perceives and understands life's problems, including their basic nature and causes, as well as the biological factors and learned patterns of response that may be contributing to a sense of hopelessness and despair. As research on problem solving has repeatedly shown, when we are frustrated by some familiar problem, we don't reach for new solutions—we reach for a bigger hammer. Unless we learn to see old problems differently, with more clarity and in less polarized terms, no new solutions can be found.

We must help suicidal people understand that the way the world seems to them is a creation of their own thinking. If the logic they use to interpret the world is flawed, their perceptions will be distorted, and they will be led to false conclusions, which can in turn prompt actions that are unnecessary, hurtful, and possibly even self-destructive. If we fail to address the cognitive distortions and skewed logic that most suicidal people fall prey to as they trudge endlessly back and forth in a deepening rut of depression and hopelessness, we can leave them with no conclusion but the one they started with: Suicide spells relief.

In general, then, my approach to working with suicidal people is to challenge, directly, a patient's *thinking*. Especially with acutely suicidal people, I am purposely not passive. A lack of assertiveness could tempt the patient to conclude that we are not about urgent business.

But make no mistake: We *are* about urgent business. We don't have all day to wonder about how things might turn out. We don't have a month to mull things over. What we are engaged in is not something cosmetic or elective. It is serious, lifesaving work. So, both physically and psychologically, I lean forward into the relationship and actively ask questions. If the process needs a leader early on, I am not at all reluctant to tackle the job.

But however directive I may be in the beginning, the work of therapy is always carried out within the context of a caring alliance between patient and healer. The protective wall built by relationships with others is the strongest safety barrier between a suicidal person and the hopelessness that could kill. Specific interventions, techniques, and strategies are the nuts and bolts of therapy, but in the absence of a genuine sense of connection—an understanding between therapist and patient that, no matter what, we're in this together—they can be all but useless.

The Therapeutic Relationship: Some Basics

A solid working relationship is not the end but the beginning of therapy. Constructing a therapeutic alliance is essential to the success of both the counselor and the patient. Much of what makes this alliance possible is already built into the therapeutic setting and into the predetermined roles that each of us brings to the relationship.

When you see a suicidal person in your role as healer, it is assumed you will do so in a private place, such as a quiet office where you will not be interrupted. In all likelihood, the two of you will also share a reasonably clear cultural understanding of what therapy is—that yours is a helping relationship, that it is something special, and that what goes on in it is confidential. If all goes well, your relationship will also be of limited duration: It will have a beginning, middle, and an end. If you want to make this relationship work, here are some basic points to keep in mind at the outset:

- ◆ Make it plain from the very start that you are on the patient's side. Most suicidal people feel that nobody is on their side—and, in some cases, no one *has* ever been on their side. So put yourself there. It's enough to say simply, "I'm on your side." Touch is important. If it seems appropriate at the end of a session, an arm around the shoulder tells your patient in the most powerful terms possible, "Hey, look, I understand, and I'm here for you." In one interesting piece of research, patients who were touched in a friendly, supportive manner by their primary care physician in the course of an appointment reported that they spent more time with their doctor than did patients who weren't touched.

◆ To encourage a sense of personal connection, arrange your interview space so that no item of furniture or other large object separates you from your patient. A big desk sitting between the two of you says, "Don't get too close." Suicidal people need to know that close is possible.

◆ Interruptions break moods, impair concentration, and cut short necessary tears. They also convey a lack of respect for the communication between healer and sufferer. So turn off your cell phone and allow no incoming calls while you are with a patient. Also make it clear that other people must not knock on the door, walk into your space, or cause any other intrusions while a session is in progress.

◆ If you can, let the patient choose the seating arrangement. "Please sit where you like" takes care of this. Depressed people often feel they have no control over anything, and so even something as simple as deciding where they would prefer to sit can be helpful. Moreover, the patient's choice of seating arrangement is sometimes suggestive. When I was in practice, I had a couch in my office—not the traditional psychoanalytic couch but an ordinary couch on which patients could sit comfortably. When I did family work, the couch often came in handy for diagnostic purposes. For instance, how close together did a troubled couple sit on their first visit?

- Similarly, talking about something as commonplace, but important, as names helps break the ice and cuts through a lot of unnecessary formalities that can hinder the building of an alliance. Ask your patient, "What would you like me to call you?" Although it is often a good sign when a patient replies with a first name, be aware that this is a matter very much influenced by culture. In addition, let the patient know right away how you would like to be addressed. Sometimes the familiarity of a first name helps early on; sometimes it doesn't. This is your call.

- Talk openly about the issue of trust. Ask your patient, "Has anyone in the past tried to help you?" If the answer is yes, find out whether the help was helpful. If your patient was at one time involved in a healing, trusting relationship, build on it. Learn about it, honor it, and keep it in mind as a counterweight to the person's current sense of hopelessness and abandonment. If, however, your patient has never received any thoughtful, compassionate help from another human being, then trust may come slowly. Especially if the patient once saw a counselor who violated a boundary, broke a confidence, or otherwise failed the patient in some way, trust is likely to be a major issue, and building trust may take a long time. Weeks, even months may pass—

but don't get discouraged. Remember that the race to healing is won not by the swift but by the persistent. One of my long-term, chronically suicidal patients told me at one point that it had taken her more than nine months to come to trust me. As I discovered, she had been sexually abused by a prior therapist, but she was able to report this to me only after she felt safe.

Finally, never finish a first session without learning something positive about your patient—a personal victory or accomplishment, or any life-affirming action, dream, or desire. You need this as much as the patient does. Suicidal patients often spend most of their initial few sessions trying to convince you what truly burdensome, loathsome creatures they are and why they should therefore be permitted to die. Neither you nor your patient can afford to be persuaded of this. No one's life is without value. She collects dolls. He once ran a marathon. She took care of her grandmother in her last days. Almost anything will do.

I remember one of the psychiatry residents at Spokane Mental Health presenting a case he was treating to our weekly case-study group. The woman he was working with had been chronically suicidal for more than twenty years and had already been treated, unsuccessfully, by a host of therapists, some of them highly experienced. His patient was very intelligent, and she was bringing him books to read about how he should approach doing therapy with someone such as herself. He was obviously frustrated and even embarrassed by his lack of progress with this woman, who was still threatening to kill herself.

At the end of his presentation, he asked the group in exasperation, "So, what do think?"

No one spoke. Finally, I asked, "Is there anything about this lady that you like?"

He thought a long moment before responding. "No," he sighed. "Not a single thing!"

I ask therapists this question for the simple reason that if you can find nothing to like or appreciate or value about a suicidal patient with whom you are working, both you and your patient are in trouble.

Bear in mind that it is the healthy, life-affirming part of the patient that joins with you in creating a therapeutic alliance. The part that wants to die cannot, and will not, do this. Each time you make a genuine human connection with a patient, you strengthen the bond between the two of you, and the risk of suicide is directly reduced. It appears that people who have close, mutually respectful, and emotionally solid and safe relationships with other people are less likely to kill themselves (Joiner 2005). Help the sufferer find, build, and sustain such relationships. The process can begin with you.

Respect for Boundaries

Many suicidal patients have been physically, sexually, and/or psychologically abused at some stage in their life. In the event that both physical and sexual abuse has occurred, the risk of suicide rises dramatically (Petronis, Samuels, Moscicki, and Anthony 1990). Abuse of any sort presupposes a fundamental lack of respect for someone's rights as an individual. It is an assault on the person's integrity and spirit. A patient who has been abused may be suffering from residual symptoms of post-traumatic stress disorder. Clearly, then, anyone who occupies the role of a healer must be supremely sensitive to personal boundaries and do nothing that might so much as hint at a possible violation of these boundaries.

Healing can take place only within a framework of mutual respect. So, if you're working to build a therapeutic alliance, don't break the rules that permit such an alliance to succeed. Here are some guidelines that should help safeguard that framework of respect:

- Don't be late for appointments. Lateness can be interpreted to mean that you don't really care or that you're angry, bored, or getting ready to give up on your patient. It can also suggest that you view your patient's time as less valuable than your own. If you absolutely cannot avoid being late, make sure you offer your apologies to your patient and explain why you were forced to be late.
- Unless you're dealing with an emergency situation, stop your counseling sessions on time. If you feel it is important to run over the hour, check to see whether this is okay with your client.
- Don't enter into any kind of relationship with your patient other than your professional one. Obviously you should never have intimate physical contact with your client, but you should also avoid any kind of personal, social, or financial situation in which the patient may be meeting your needs instead of the other way around.
- It's fine to accept thank-yous, but you should refrain from accepting gifts for your work. Even seemingly trivial gifts from patients carry invisible price tags. Accepting a gift, especially an expensive or otherwise special one, creates a sense of obligation in the therapist and can confound the counseling process, thereby jeopardizing both sufferer and healer.
- If you are charging fees to your patient, don't allow a substantial bill to accumulate. Owing your therapist a pile of money is a good reason to stop therapy. A large debt could even prove to be

the last straw for a suicidal person, the excuse he or she needs to call it quits.

Keeping the boundaries of the therapeutic framework clear and fair will ensure the best possible working situation for both you and your patient. Of course, there may be times when you feel that bending the rules a little would be helpful. But such exceptions should be made only with due consideration, preferably after consultation with a more experienced colleague or, if you are in training, under supervision. Your patient's safety is yours to protect, and you can do this only if your standards of practice are ethical and respectful of your patient's integrity—and your own.

Keeping a Sense of Balance

Even with all we have learned about suicide and about the effectiveness of specific therapies, understanding and treating suicidal patients remains as much an art as a science. What we do isn't physics, and it bears not the least resemblance to the symmetry of math or the predictable syntax of chemistry. Given our limitations, not the least of which is the subjective element in what we do, we are sometimes forced to make treatment decisions in a frustrating haze of uncertainty. At best, what we do is guided by evidence-based practices, by our experience, and by a certain amount of educated guesswork. At worst, we have to rely on uneducated guesswork.

In view of our imperfect knowledge, and because we are only human, no matter how hard we try we are going to make our share of mistakes. You may let a therapy session slip out of control. You may say something impossibly insensitive or ignorant. You may forget to ask a critical question (which will probably come to you twenty minutes after the session has ended). And, most assuredly, you will at some point assume something that is not so.

But that's okay. As long as the goal of saving a life is uppermost in your mind, don't worry. Suicidal patients are typically desperate for some shred of hope. Rather than grading your performance for adequacy, they are much more likely to study your face for sincerity, for some sign that you believe their lives are not as hopeless as they have come to believe them to be. If you make a mistake and quickly own it, your patient is likely to forgive you much more readily than you may be willing to forgive yourself.

So abandon the myth of perfect practice. Remember that you aren't a god but a fallible human being. For this reason, never let a suicidal patient cast you in the role of savior. Allowing yourself to become the one and only person in the world who can rescue the suicidal person from self-destruction places both of you at risk. Being idealized is one step away from being worshiped—and being worshiped is one step away from falling from grace.

It helps to be clear in your own mind about who has the final responsibility. Presumably you have already resolved that no suicidal patient is going to die with your permission and that you intend to do all you possibly can to prevent this person from taking his or her own life. But suicidal patients will sometimes try to convince you that their life is entirely in your hands. This is simply not true. When all is said and done, each of us is responsible for what we decide. If, in the end, a patient chooses suicide, that is his choice or her choice, not yours.

Be sure you understand that, then, even though you do your very best, someone you are working with could die by suicide. It happens, even to the most skilled and experienced clinicians. Emergency room physicians do not save everybody they see, and neither do counselors. Consider that if we ever succeeded in getting all the suicidal people who live in our communities into treatment, the total number of deaths among patients receiving inpatient or outpatient care would probably go up, simply because there would be a larger number of suicidal people in treatment overall. And this would be a good thing. At least then every suicidal person would have the opportunity to benefit from potentially lifesaving interventions. Even if getting everyone into treatment meant that, in the shorter term, we had more patients dying on us, we might see our base rates for suicide start to fall.

The Placebo Effect

There is an element of faith in all healing. Because you are a healer, the mere fact of your qualifications, along with your presence and your attention to the patient's problems, can have a beneficial impact on symptoms. If a suffering patient believes that he or she is going to feel better after having talked to you, he or she probably will. I call this the placebo effect.

As a healer, you are a merchant of hope, and so the sufferer will already have some degree of faith in you before he or she ever enters your office. And because you are a trained professional, your patient will tend to assume that you are honest, trustworthy, courageous, and loyal—as well as smart. After all, you've presumably read a lot of books about the human condition (including this one). Smart therapists allow the suffering patient to believe that he or she is in good hands. This belief is critical to the rekindling of hope.

It stands to reason, then, that you don't want to do anything that might undermine the benefits to be had from your status as a healer. There are many things you can do to foul up your placebo effect: Doze off, fiddle with paperwork or otherwise seem uninterested in what the patient is saying, be overly abrupt or impatient, take phone calls during a session, or ask questions that suggest you haven't been paying attention. Don't do these things.

In addition, because you're the professional, your personal appearance matters. You should always look neat and dress appropriately, according to the standards set by your place of work and the culture more generally. Your office also speaks volumes about you, so make sure it doesn't convey the wrong message. Check it out. Do you have silly or potentially offensive posters on display? If you have plants, do they look healthy and well cared for? Is there anything on the walls or desk that might add to the patient's sense of failure or disillusionment? Does the place exude warmth, or does it send off a bureaucratic, we-don't-care-much-about-people chill? If you don't know how your office décor comes across, ask a few people whom you can trust to give you an honest opinion.

Of course, patients are more likely to have confidence in you if you appear to believe in what you're doing. Among other things, when you are working with a patient, especially an actively suicidal one, it is critically important that you not seem ambivalent or uncertain about the nature, purpose, and power of therapy and of appropriate medications. Hundreds of lives are saved each day by both words and medicines and, above all, by wonderfully sustaining combinations of the two. So be bold. Sow hope where none grows.

Therapy does work! Certain schools of thought and practice may be temporarily in the ascendant; others may fall from favor. But a fundamental faith in healing and healers is essential for suicidal patients. Without a belief in the possibility of a cure, hope dies. A therapist who is clearly confident about the benefits of therapy enables the patient to find hope for the future—to believe that, no matter how deep the present despair, someday life is going to feel worth living for.

The faith our patients have in us is a precious commodity. It gives them the willingness to believe what we say and do what we suggest. Yes, you will make your share of mistakes, but at least try to avoid making the obvious ones. Don't hand a patient reasons to question that faith.

Naming the Demon

People go to professional healers to get answers. The first and most important question to which they need an answer is, "What's wrong with me?" The anxiety born of uncertainty multiplies the pain a person is experiencing. A clear diagnosis—however grave the ailment—can reduce this anxiety. Therapists and counselors have the power to name the demon, and naming the demon is the first step toward healing.

Naming the demon reassures the sufferer that, if nothing else, someone knows what is wrong. It also inspires hope—because if someone knows what's wrong, it can probably be put right again. In addition, putting a name to the problem assures the patient that you paid attention to what he or she had to say. Bear in mind that talking with you may be the first open and straightforward communication the patient has had with anyone in a long time. The knowledge that we have been heard and understood dramatically reduces feelings of confusion and despair.

The diagnosis is, of course, critical to the treatment you will recommend to the patient. So, before arriving at a final diagnosis, you should always carry out a thorough and careful assessment. But while it is important not to jump to any conclusions, it is also important to offer some sort of tentative description of the problem at the end of an initial session. By the end of the first hour, after you have taken the patient's history, you will usually have a pretty good idea about how to name the problem. You don't have to be certain, but you can say, "Given what you've told me, I wonder whether what is going on is . . ."

In making your diagnosis, you need to give some thought to the way it is phrased. If your patient feels uncomfortable with the terminology you use, he or she might resist the diagnosis, at which point you may have difficulty getting the patient to accept treatment. I once saw a seriously depressed police officer who was having suicidal thoughts. He had all the classic symptoms that accompany a major depressive episode, but I suspected he might reject the word *depression* as a description of his feelings. So I asked him to tell me, in his own words, what he thought was wrong. "Well," he began, "I think I have a broken give-a-shitter."

The language of diagnosis can take many forms. For some patients, a formal, medical-sounding statement works best ("You have what the *Diagnostic and Statistical Manual of the American Psychiatric Association* terms a major depressive disorder"). In other cases, something less sophisticated might be more effective ("You know what, kid? You're stuck in Blues City"). A favorite of mine—useful for, say, clinically depressed young men who are thinking of killing themselves because a relationship has just ended—is: "What you're going through here is what we call open heart surgery without benefit of anesthetic." If I get a laugh (however grim), I know I have just accomplished the most important thing a diagnosis does: separates the sufferer from the source of the pain.

Monitoring the Treatment Plan

As I have argued elsewhere, one of the difficulties with treating suicidal patients is that suicidal thoughts and feelings, and likewise suicide planning and attempts, are a symptom, not a diagnosis. Because suicidality is only one symptom among many, such as impaired sleep, weight loss, or irritability, when it comes to monitoring a patient's response to treatment it is all too easy to regard suicidality as on a par with other symptoms. This is a dangerous temptation—given that suicide is the most probable cause of premature death in someone who is already suicidal. Rather, suicidal ideation should be constantly tracked and evaluated as the key indicator of a patient's therapeutic progress (or lack thereof).

It is not uncommon for therapists who have had a patient die by suicide while in treatment to admit that they were not aware that their patient was suicidal at the time. The sad truth is that we can all too easily be lulled into believing that patients are no longer at risk when in fact they are. It could be that the therapist never asked the S question in the first place, and so the subject of suicide was never explored. Or it could be that after a period of improvement the patient has once again become suicidal but has given no clear indication of the downturn.

I am convinced that during relapses into depression and in some cases substance abuse, our patients—especially those who happen to like us—often do not wish to burden us with the fact that our medicine and our psychotherapeutic interventions apparently aren't working. They may also feel a sense of failure, and so they are embarrassed to admit that they're feeling worse, not better. This leaves it to us to make sure that nothing escapes our attention.

This may seem obvious, but even though it is the patient who is ultimately responsible for his or her life, the therapist must assume ultimate responsibility for control over the therapy. This means taking charge, asking questions, digging for facts, and scouring the emotional landscape for glimmerings of hope or other evidence of change. It means listening well and long, closely observing actions and reactions, and never assuming you know something you actually do not know. It also means following up on any action or remark—no matter how subtle—that even hints that things are not going well.

Remember that therapy is a fluid process, one in which the various twists and turns cannot always be anticipated. This being the case, it simply makes good sense to take stock of a patient's progress from time to time. Not only does this sort of routine checking give depth and nuance to your working alliance, but it also allows you to revisit the treatment plan, if need be. As things change—for better or worse—so should the course of treatment.

Repeated reassessments of risk, symptoms, and clinical status over the course of treatment are in fact one of the hallmarks of competent counseling. All you need to do is ask, "So how are we doing? Have you had any thoughts about suicide this past week?" Asking this question now and then, after the initial suicide crisis has passed, lets the patient know you haven't forgotten the reason for his or her original visit. It also gives you a little added insurance against missing a clue that the patient's condition has worsened. So never sit and wonder whether a once suicidal person is again suicidal. Ask and you will know. If you query a patient so frequently about possible suicidal feelings that he or she finally complains, "Would you stop being so worried about me?" you can always apologize and say, "I'm just double checking—because I care about you."

When you reassess a patient for current suicide risk, always try to record in his or her chart something the person recently said ("Nope, I haven't thought about suicide in weeks," for example). Also make note of any changes in positive or negative symptoms and in the patient's life situation, particularly its sources of stress. Such chart entries are a matter of due diligence, as well as a sensible precaution. But they also remind you to stay on target—to make sure the primary issue you are addressing in treatment remains clearly in sight.

Healers Matter
Despite the unquestionable value of such miracles as antipsychotic, anti-anxiety, and antidepressant medications, it is still often necessary for people who have talked

themselves into suicide to be talked out of it again. Helping people doesn't get any tougher than working with folks who want to die. If we, who seek to heal, are to do this work well, we need to know something not only about our patients but about ourselves.

It is my strongly held belief that, whatever the underlying illness or precipitating event, the treatment of suicidal people is fundamentally the treatment of hopelessness, a hopelessness born of unremitting and unendurable psychological pain. Hopelessness is a psychological state in which the sufferer believes that *nothing positive will ever happen again*. This overwhelming affective and cognitive state is contagious—to other people who are vulnerable to suicidal thinking, certainly, but also to healers.

If you have ever worked with someone who is seriously suicidal, you may already understand what I mean. When someone has just spent an hour presenting a seemingly airtight case as to why life is no longer worth living, and in the end you find yourself beginning to agree, then you know that therapists are not immune to the contagion of hopelessness. Rule number one in working with suicidal people? The therapist must survive the process. If, after working with someone suicidal, you notice yourself feeling oddly impotent or ineffective, consider the possibility that you've been persuaded to become an unconscious co-conspirator in your client's suicide. If the patient is helpless and then convinces you that you are helpless, then you will *both be hopeless*.

You need to inoculate yourself against this contagion. Because as soon as you become as pessimistic about your patient's prospects as he or she is—or come to believe, as your patient does, that life is not worth living—you are likely to be part of the problem, not the solution.

Doing therapy with someone produces strong feelings; it's supposed to. If we wish to do our work well, especially over the long haul of a professional career, we need to take good care of our own emotional health, and this means learning to manage the feelings we have toward our patients. Up to a point, this is something we can do on our own, but there will be times when we need to turn to others for advice and support. In my experience, anyone who works with suicidal people would do well to keep in mind the following:

- If you find yourself feeling inadequate and anxious as you prepare to meet a suicidal patient, talk this over with your colleagues. You need to understand your anxiety and where it's coming from. Fear is never wrong, and seeking to understand is always right.
- Fully expect to experience strong emotions both during and after sessions. But also be aware that, in an effort to step out of the emotional vortex that an acutely distressed patient can create, therapists sometimes allow their minds to wander or otherwise retreat emotionally while they are with a patient. This is to be expected. Be sure you know when it is happening.
- The instant you feel yourself becoming bored with a suicidal patient, find a panic button to hit. These feelings could take the form of a passing thought that this patient might do better in group therapy. Or you might find yourself thinking that the patient should perhaps be transferred to a new resident or a therapist in training, someone who would welcome the chance to work on the case. But no matter how your feelings of boredom find expression, you need to discuss them with a supervisor or colleague. In all likelihood, what is happening is

that you are unconsciously pulling back from your therapeutic engagement and reducing your investment in the patient. This subtle withdrawal of your emotional connection will not go unnoticed by the suicidal person, and it could put a life in jeopardy.

- The instant you feel any anger toward a suicidal patient, find two panic buttons to push. Feeling angry with a patient you once got along with, and even liked, is proof positive that something has gone wrong with the therapy. Again, you should talk your feelings over with a colleague or supervisor with a view to determining their cause.

- Periodically, have a look at whether you are managing your suicidal patients the same way you do your other patients. Have you taken to scheduling appointments at all hours for these patients? Have you been accepting 3 A.M. phone calls even when no crisis exists? Have you agreed to call patients once a day to make sure they're okay? If you have, then once again it is time to sit down with a colleague or supervisor and take a good hard look at your sense of balance.

Finally, it is my conviction that humor is empowering. I am not referring to jokes made at the patient's expense but to humor anchored in the compassion that is fundamental to the work we do. Humor gives us a sudden, sure distance from the source of our pain. It allows us to think the unthinkable and to chuckle at an old line from W. C. Fields: "Life's a funny old business, and you're lucky to get out alive."

I am in fact convinced that humor shared between two people is absolutely incompatible with serious thoughts of suicide. I once interviewed an alcoholic logger who had been hospitalized after driving his truck off a cliff in a drunken suicidal rage. I asked him how it was possible that he was still alive. "Well, I was so drunk," he told me, "I picked the wrong cliff. It was only two feet high." Then he laughed. "If I'd have been sober, I'd have found a much higher cliff. And now *you* want *me* to quit drinking!"

We both laughed. And both of us felt a lot better.

There is no darker subject than self-destruction. But, as someone once said, wit is the only thing between us and the dark.

CHAPTER 5
Therapeutic Interventions

IN THE THERAPEUTIC WORLD, the trend is now toward "manualized" treatments grounded in science. But there are any number of strategies that can be employed in doing therapy. Up to a point, these strategies can be taught and learned, and a well-trained therapist is familiar with a wide range of techniques on which he or she can draw. What cannot be so easily taught is the intuitive sense of which strategies to use with whom, and when. This intuitive understanding is perhaps the essence of the healer's art, and it comes chiefly through experience.

The ideas and suggestions that follow have been culled from the literature, picked up in lectures, and taught to me by colleagues and patients. One of these patients was a woman named Mary.

Mary was in her early forties when I met her. For the past twenty years she had suffered from a major depressive disorder. She had twice overdosed and had nearly died on both occasions. Antidepressants had failed to provide sufficient relief. Hospitalizations only humiliated her. Mary was utterly pessimistic, all but bereft of hope. She was also intelligent—and clever to the point of nearly convincing me she ought to go ahead and die.

Working closely with a psychiatrist colleague, I treated Mary weekly for three years before she began to make a recovery. She and I often clashed over the merits of living, and on some days she begged me to give up on her and let her go. But I didn't quit. And neither did Mary. She is now a grandmother of four and for over two decades has been doing fine.

What Mary, and others like her, taught me about the suicidal mind—about the dark interior landscape through which the sufferer must travel and about how one endures the bouts of utter despair born of psychological pain so intense that it is felt physically—were lessons from life I could have learned nowhere else.

As to the observations and strategies that follow, no single rationale or theory underlies them all, although I have tried to provide an explanation for each of the suggestions I make—some sense of why, in my experience, the approach is effective. Obviously, though, not every technique is appropriate for every patient. To some extent, it will be clear from the nature of the intervention whether it is likely to be helpful to a specific person. Beyond that, your own best judgment will have to be your guide.

But if no two patients are alike, neither are any two therapists. If you feel that a particular line of questioning or a specific maneuver, scheme, or ploy is not well suited to your personality and established style, then don't use it. At least some of these approaches, however, should work for just about anybody.

1. Empowering the Patient

If you accept the premise that some suicidal people are suicidal because they feel helpless, overwhelmed, and out of control, then anything a therapist can do to combat the feelings that feed a sense of powerlessness will be a plus. Here are several relatively simple things you can do to enhance the patient's sense of command:

◆ Provided there is no urgent crisis, allow the patient to pick the time of your appointments.

You each have schedules, but unless it matters greatly to you, or unless you have a standing appointment with the patient, give the patient a choice. Looking at my schedule, I might say, "What's the best day for you?" Or, if things are looking tight in my schedule, "I have an opening at 10:00 Thursday morning and another in the afternoon, at 2:00. Which would you prefer?"

◆ Unless you feel strongly that you would do better always to see the person alone, invite your patient to bring his or her significant other along to at least one session. More often than not, a suicide crisis revolves around two people. Much can be learned from bringing the second person into a session, and opening this door can be empowering.

◆ When a patient is unwilling to share some deep dark secret that you believe could help you understand what is going on, don't be too insistent. You can shift control to the person by saying, "Look, I understand that maybe you just can't talk about this right away. That's okay. You can always tell me about it later, when you feel ready." Except for an active suicide plan, most other secrets can wait.

◆ If it feels right and is clinically sound, consider giving the patient the power to phone you at your personal number, if need be. This is your choice, and whether the option will extend to weekends and evenings, or even the middle of the night, is something you can work out together. I make it clear with suicidal patients that therapy happens in the office, not on the telephone. But I also make it clear that I expect them to pack my phone number, not a pistol. (Of course, if the suicidal person is in a crisis, you must ensure that multiple access routes to safety are available and wide open.)

- Another useful approach is to look at each day as a series of opportunities to make choices, from what socks you pull on in the morning to the last thing you read before going to sleep. Walking someone through these decisions and encouraging the person to make different choices sometimes, just for the hell of it, can give a seriously depressed patient a much needed sense of personal control.

Patients are apt to feel especially powerless about the decision to try medication. Not all patients who are prescribed antidepressants or other psychotropic drugs are eager to take them. Some patients simply forget, some don't like the side effects, some just don't like drugs. Suicidal people present a special problem. If they take the medication they've been prescribed, this suggests to them that they've decided to live, and some patients are initially too ambivalent to make this decision.

It is thus important that you spend as much time as necessary to convince a patient that a recommended medical treatment plan will make a real difference. I will often say, "Believe me, these medications work. They'll help you sleep. Your mood will start to improve in a couple of weeks or so. If things work right, you'll get some energy back and begin to feel better. But they won't stop you from killing yourself. Only you can make that decision. In the meantime, let me give you some information about depression so that you can learn a little about the illness and its treatment." Providing patients with the facts about a proposed medication frequently proves very helpful. If it seems appropriate to do so, you can also refer patients to Web sites that you've reviewed where they can find answers to commonly asked questions concerning specific drugs.

Because involving patients in the decision to begin medication allows them to feel some measure of control, it tends to improve their rate of adherence. It doesn't change the therapy agreement, but it indicates that you respect the patient's intelligence and his or her right to participate in treatment decisions. It also serves to remind patients that, as always, they are the ones ultimately responsible for their own welfare.

2. Givens and Not-Givens

Certain factors that contribute to suicide risk are beyond our power to influence. A psychiatric disorder or other chronic illness, a prior suicide attempt, a family history of depression, gray, overcast skies—factors such as these are not under our control. What we *can* control is our attitude toward these givens and our ability to reflect on the meaning they hold for us.

One of the main goals of cognitive-behavioral therapy is to bring about fundamental shifts in a suicidal person's way of thinking, including his or her perceptions of life's givens. At the same time, such therapy helps a patient develop a sense of control over those areas of his or her life that are not given. Not-givens include relationships, jobs, hobbies and other personal interests, diet, exercise, and rest and relaxation. But they also include our emotions. It can easily seem that our feelings—especially painful ones such as jealousy, anger, hatred, a sense of abandonment or rejection, and the desire for revenge—simply happen to us. In truth, however, the way we think goes a long way toward determining how we feel.

A good exercise here is to have the patient make up two lists, of givens and not-givens. Such an exercise obliges a patient to evaluate what truly is immutable and can thus provide a useful focus for the patient's thoughts and energy as he or she struggles to make changes. These changes may include giving up efforts to change the unchangeable. One of my patients, a woman who had been angry and disappointed with her mother for the past twenty-five years, ultimately decided that her mother belonged in the "givens" column because, as she put it, "She is never going to change, and I might as well stop trying to fix her."

Perhaps the most important of the not-givens, however, is what we choose to believe is the nature and ultimate purpose of a human being. This is a tough and complex subject, but it has been my experience that suicidal people can benefit greatly from learning to reflect on philosophical issues as part of a reevaluation of their reasons for living or dying. Young people, especially, often have little experience with stopping and thinking a matter through. Therapy can show them how to do this. As the thoughtful therapist who questions just how smart it really is to kill yourself, you serve as a model for the adolescent, who learns to adopt a more critical perspective on his or her thoughts.

The overarching aim of therapy is nothing less than teaching someone to become more psychologically observant and analytical so that he or she can, one day, become his or her own therapist. As part of this process, the patient learns to think differently about the problems of living and, into the bargain, find ways to fix what is fixable and let go of the rest. In my view, there is no better preparation for the vicissitudes of life than a good working personal philosophy. Therapy can help a suicidal person find one.

3. Diet and Exercise

Among the general recommendations you can make to suicidal people are a few that can hardly fail to be helpful, for the simple reason that following these recommendations is virtually certain to enhance mood and promote a sense of well-being. These commonsense suggestions include getting enough sound sleep, eating a balanced and nutritious diet, drinking plenty of water, and making time for relaxation and recreation.

What we eat and drink plays a large part in how our bodies and minds function and in how we feel. And, as we all know, a walk or a light workout produces positive changes in body chemistry. According to *Physical Activity and Health: A Report from the Surgeon General* (U.S. Department of Health and Human Services 1996), even three ten-minute periods of light exercise each day will significantly improve one's physical health. Particularly in view of the lethargy and overall lack of motivation that accompany depression, however, suicidal people are rarely getting adequate exercise.

They also tend to be eating too little of what we know is good for us and/or too much of what we know is not. Early on in my work with someone who is suicidal I therefore make a point of asking a few questions about their eating habits and, if need be, referring them to a dietician. Although some physicians are attentive to diet, many are not. A dietician is a specialist and can be counted on to evaluate everything from sugar intake to coffee consumption.

In addition, I typically encourage patients to set up a regular schedule of light exercise. Bear in mind, though, that when someone has previously been sedentary, a program of exercise—be it a home stretching and movement program, a few laps around the track, a daily walk down a country road, or a yoga class—may need to be undertaken gradually. Especially in the case of an older patient or one who has had health problems, you should be sure the patient's doctor knows and approves of any potentially vigorous efforts at physical training.

Even if getting some exercise appears to be small medicine for a big problem, it represents a change in daily routine and can constitute a powerful affirmation of life. It also increases opportunities for social contact and may serve to interrupt ruminations about suicide. Similarly, the fact that you are paying attention to your patient's diet—to what they use to sustain life—conveys a message of caring and hope. You want this person to live.

4. HALT

Every action occurs twice, once when we first think of it and then again when we actually carry it out. To get from the thought to the action we must pass over a threshold. Like any other action, then, an act of suicide requires that a suicidal person cross the threshold between thought and deed.

Even people who are severely depressed do not live in constant and imminent danger of stepping across the threshold between the thought of suicide and the act itself. Many protective factors stand as barriers at that threshold. These factors intervene between the moment the thought of suicide first comes to mind and the final action of reaching for a knife or gun or fashioning a noose and throwing the rope over a rafter.

Among the factors that afford some protection against suicide is a sense of well-being, which is to some degree dependent on states of mind and body over which we have considerable control. Elevated levels of agitation and anxiety, especially in combination with sleeplessness, can easily produce a frame of mind in which protective factors are weakened, making it more likely that a suicidal person will cross the threshold between thought and action. Anything we can do to enhance overall mood therefore helps reduce risk.

The acronym HALT was borrowed from the recovery program of Alcoholics Anonymous and the literature on relapse prevention. "HALT" stands for "hungry, angry, lonely, tired." If any of these states of mind and body are allowed to develop in an alcoholic or addict, he or she is in greater danger of moving from the idea of taking a drink or drug to the action of doing so. When, instead, the person has eaten, is feeling reasonably relaxed and content, is in the company of friends, and is well rested, these positive conditions strengthen the buffer between thought and action, thereby reducing the risk of relapse.

Similarly, someone who is severely depressed is more likely to cross the threshold to suicide when he or she is hungry, angry, lonely or tired. And this is doubly true for a suicidal addict or alcoholic. Once someone suffering from both depression and alcoholism or addiction is over the threshold to that first drink or drug and becomes intoxicated, the risk of a suicide attempt skyrockets. As I said earlier, and will say again, there is no safety without sobriety—and there is absolutely no safety for a suicidal person who is hungry, angry, lonely, tired, and drunk.

So teach your suicidal patient these four things:

- If you're hungry, fix a snack or eat a meal.
- If you're angry, count to ten, walk around the block, or find a way to forgive and forget.
- If you're lonely, call or visit a friend or family member (and/or get to an Alcoholics Anonymous or Narcotics Anonymous meeting).
- If you're tired, take a nap.

Of all the practical suggestions offered in this text, these are the easiest and most effective ways to head off a suicide attempt. In fact, Alcoholics Anonymous has probably prevented more suicides than any other organization in the world.

Following this simple advice accomplishes three key things: It puts control over one's state of mind directly into the hands of the sufferer, it reduces the risk of conflict with others, and it helps restore a state of mind that is fundamentally incompatible with the wish to die. If abiding by this advice seems unworkable to the suicidal person, a serious reassessment of risk is in order. You need to ask yourself:

Is this person too anxious to sleep?

Is this person so isolated that there is no friend or family member with whom he or she can spend a little time?

Is this person in so much pain or so angry and irritable that he or she can not make effective use of self-soothing exercises?

If the answer to any of these questions is yes, and the patient is still contemplating suicide, then inpatient hospitalization should be considered.

I once had the sad task of reviewing the suicide of a 42-year-old man. At the time of his death, he had not eaten for almost two days, and so he was *hungry*; he was *angry* because his wife had thrown him out of the house and had filed for divorce; he was *lonely* because he had been denied access to his children and had lost a close friend in recent weeks; and he was *tired* because he had been up most of the night in an emergency room undergoing a psychiatric evaluation after he threatened to kill himself. Now add to all this the fact that he was an alcoholic who had recently relapsed. It was no surprise to learn that when he shot himself in the early morning hours, following his discharge from the hospital, his blood alcohol level was twice the legal limit. We cannot know whether this man would still be alive if he had known about HALT. But it is at least possible that he would not have relapsed, which might in turn have prevented the final downward spiral to suicide.

5. One Day at a Time

Coaching suicidal people to live one day at a time—reminding them that they just need to make it through the current twenty-four hours—can help them make it through a bad day. But it can also give them a tool with which to counter one of the cognitive distortions that often attend depressed and suicidal people. To appreciate the value of this approach, you need to understand how suicidal people see the future.

Ask the question, "What are your plans for next week?" and many suicidal people won't have an answer. Ask the question, "What will you be doing this time next year?" and you're likely to get a blank stare.

People who are so seriously depressed as to be suicidal typically suffer from a narrow and foreshortened view of the future, one in which pessimism rules. If they are swift to draw negative conclusions from almost any circumstance, they do so simply because they are unable to imagine any other conclusions. This distorted perspective, this view of one's self and one's world as lacking in any real worth or promise, leads to a negation of the future tense. Suicidal people can't think about the future or invest a dollar's worth of hope therein when the present seems unbearable. They can't imagine a better tomorrow when they can't get out of bed today, nor can they dream of happy endings when the sweet smell of flowers conjures up a funeral.

In the eyes of those who are suicidally depressed, other people seem to live in the lovely, lighthearted world of a musical, full of bursts of color and song, while they are trapped in the black-and-white world of film noir. Worse yet, the picture jerks, stops, starts, and stops again, and the popcorn is stale. To someone stuck neck deep in the rut of a serious depression, staying alive for even a few more days may seem impossible. But staying alive one more day is doable.

Living one day at a time is a plan, and most likely a workable plan. You may not be able to get a suicidal patient to imagine the end of next week. But you can probably get them to imagine the rest of today. Then, tomorrow morning, they can focus on getting through the next one day. As the days go by, and therapy progresses, living through the entire next week will start to seem possible.

When a patient has plans for the future, this is powerful evidence that the person is beginning to heal. I knew one of my chronically depressed patients was finally getting better when she told me at the end of a session, "You know, come May, I may take a trip to see my sister." Evidently, she was planning to be alive in the spring. As it was only January, this was wonderful news.

6. Driving a Wedge

To the suicidal sufferer, psychological pain takes the form of a relentless series of awful ideas, uncontrollable thoughts, and agonizing feelings. Even though the pain, the psychache, may come in episodes, overall it seems endless and unbroken. An initial diagnosis—saying to a patient, "Look, here's what's causing all this pain"—drives a wedge into the seamlessness of suffering. It puts a border around the big problem and fixes it in one place, so that the patient can step back and look at it. Then, once the patient is able to identify the main problem, the two of you can start in on the smaller problems that are currently overwhelming the patient.

By driving wedges in the form of additional diagnostic and fact-finding questions, you can begin to parse psychological pain, to divide it into segments that the patient can examine one by one. Driving a wedge separates the sufferer from the source of pain. This process gradually leads to a better understanding of the pain, of where it is coming from, and of the faces it wears. Once a suicidal person gets some distance on present problems and life circumstances, he or she will begin to feel better.

Here are some handy wedges worth driving:

◆ *This is the way depressed people feel. But this isn't the way you've always felt, is it?* This asks the patient to affirm the existence of an earlier self, one that felt more optimistic about life.
◆ *When you feel this bad, where exactly does it hurt?* This situates the pain somewhere, which often makes it

seem less all-encompassing and hence more manageable. Sometimes suicidal people will say that the pain is everywhere in their body, but more often they will locate it in their head or in their heart. Rating the intensity of the pain is also helpful. Those who work in pain management rank physical pain on a scale from 1 (mild) to 10 (intolerable), and the same scale can be used for psychological pain. Pain management is only possible when we can talk about the pain we are feeling, and assigning it a location and a level of severity makes it easier to talk about.

◆ *When you feel the very worst, whose name or face comes to mind?* This may produce a roster of people with whom the patient is in conflict and can open the door to productive relationship counseling.

◆ *What finally happened the last time you went through a period like this?* This asks the patient to recall having survived an earlier crisis. The answer may also alert you to some of the protective factors that are available to the patient, such as close friends, supportive family members, a pastor or priest, or possibly a former therapist, and perhaps provide information about other resources that can be brought to bear on the present situation.

◆ *Given all that's happened to you lately, can you really trust your thoughts?* This helps the sufferer accept the possibility that he or she is not thinking all that clearly right at the moment and that it might be wise to take some time before making any life-and-death decisions.

◆ *You seem angry enough to kill yourself. Did you get this angry all by yourself?* This refocuses attention to external sources of frustration and away from self-blame (a common experience of depressed people).

- *If you tend to think of suicide when you're drunk, is booze really your friend?* This casts doubt on the idea that alcohol is a useful remedy for depression.
- *Because your father killed himself, does this mean you have to?* This challenges the conclusion that heredity provides a mandate for suicide.
- *It doesn't seem fair for your mother [father, lover, husband, wife, child] to cause you this much pain? But did they really intend to?* This question encourages the patient to examine the motives he or she attributes to others and consider whether they are accurate.
- *You understand that the kind of pain you're in doesn't last forever. So if you knew someone who was feeling as miserable as you do right now, would you advise this person to kill himself or herself?* This brings about a shift in perspective, putting the patient in the role of the wise healer rather than the helpless sufferer.

In addition to putting some distance between the person and the psychological pain in which he or she has been immersed, a good wedge-driving question causes the suicidal person to rethink conclusions already drawn, some of which will surely be wrong. Such questions open up gaps in the constricted circles of logic that have led the person to consider suicide.

You know you're asking good clinical questions when your patient says things like "I'm getting confused" or "I hadn't thought of it that way." Or when your patient falls silent. Such responses are pure clinical gold. I sometimes tell patients I've just tripped up by driving a wedge, "You're confused? That's great! Now we're getting somewhere!"

7. Bibliotherapy
Odd though it might seem, suicidal patients can sometimes profit from reading about suicide. Books are anoth-

er way of driving a wedge, of giving a suffering patient a new perspective on his or her experience, which helps to separate the person from what feels like endless and all-encompassing pain. There are many informative and life-affirming books about suicide that you can recommend to patients. More are being written all the time, so the list provided here is hardly definitive.

Thomas Ellis and Cory Newman's *Choosing to Live: How to Defeat Suicide Through Cognitive Therapy* is an evidence-based, self-help approach designed to teach suicidal people how to understand the sources of the thinking and feelings that lead someone to consider suicide. The book also features a step-by-step guide to recovery that can serve as a useful adjunct to therapy. My own book *Suicide: The Forever Decision*, is addressed directly to the suicidal sufferer and takes the form of an extended therapy session. It is available worldwide as an e-book, in several languages and at no cost.

Anyone interested in a sympathetic, highly readable personal account of what it feels like to be suicidally depressed should read William Styron's *Darkness Visible: A Memoir of Madness*. I can also highly recommend *Lincoln's Melancholy: How Depression Challenged a President and Fueled His Greatness*, by Joshua Wolf Shenk, which contains a fascinating discussion of Abraham Lincoln's struggles with depression and suicidal thinking. Kay Redfield Jamison's *Night Falls Fast: Understanding Suicide* offers what is perhaps the ideal blend of good writing, solid science, and in-depth information about suicide. Jamison, who suffers from bipolar disorder and once made a serious suicide attempt herself, is one of the most highly respected experts in the field, and her writing is superb.

Three first-rate books for young people and their families are Bev Cobain's *When Nothing Matters Anymore: A Survival Guide for Depressed Teens*, David Fassler and Lynne Dumas's *"Help Me I'm Sad": Recognizing, Treating, and Preventing Childhood*

Depression, and Andrew Slaby and Lili Frank Garfinkel's *No One Saw My Pain: Why Teens Kill Themselves*. Other books aimed at youth are coming on the market almost every month, and I encourage you to keep an eye open for them, read them, and, if they seem to you worthwhile, recommend them to parents and other family members, as well as to patients.

In addition to the many excellent books that can prove therapeutic to suicidal patients are a few that could be antitherapeutic, such as Derek Humphry's *Final Exit: The Practicalities of Self-Deliverance and Assisted Suicide for the Dying*. Although Humphry's best-selling book concerns the right of the terminally ill to choose the time and place of their death, the information it provides about the various methods for ending one's life could be dangerous to suicidal individuals. Such literature is hardly good medicine for someone who is ambivalent about living. When you first begin working with a suicidal patient, you would be wise to determine whether he or she has been reading books about euthanasia or is involved in a suicide chat group on the Internet.

8. Blocked Exits

The term *blocked exit* refers to a situation in which someone believes that there is no means of escape from a set of circumstances that he or she perceives as intolerable. Faced with her infidelity to her husband and a massive burden of debt, Madame Bovary swallows arsenic. As she says on her deathbed, "There were no other possibilities."

A man of high reputation who has been engaged in fraud is threatened with a humiliating public exposure. A woman who suffers from clinical depression and an addiction to heroin is arrested for prostitution, has her children removed from her care, and is detained against her will in a psychiatric facility. For someone who is mentally ill, the intolerable and inescapable situation may be the apparently self-imposed yet nonetheless exquisite torture of his or her own mind. In circumstances such as these, the sufferer feels trapped in the experience of severe and seemingly interminable psychological pain, pain that cannot be relieved by any means known to the sufferer save death.

Typically, the blocked exit is composed of a series of blocked exits. Imagine yourself in a movie theater beginning to watch a film—but the movie isn't the one you were expecting. It's a horror film, and it's terrifying beyond all belief. All you want to do is get out of there, but on testing one exit you discover it's locked. So is the second, and the third, and the fourth. Rushing to one remaining door, you find it padlocked. There's no way out. You close your eyes, but you can still hear the screams of the victims on the screen. Panic strikes.

This is the way life often feels to suicidal people. They've searched for ways out of their growing fear, anger, and despair and their rising sense of panic. But they haven't found any.

Sometimes, of course, our circumstances genuinely are inescapable. We have little choice but to accept them and deal with them as best we can—which generally does not include killing ourselves over them. But suicidal people are frequently unable to see a way through a difficult situation other than suicide. This inability to come up with alternatives is symptomatic of the impaired cognitive functioning characteristic of the depressed mind. As we know, depressed people who have a history of suicidal ideation perform poorly at problem solving (Williams, Barnhofer, Crane, and Beck 2005). Creative solutions are simply not available. New paths do not open up. Combine this inability to think outside the box with increasing levels of agitation and anxiety, and suicide becomes the awful but only escape.

The therapist's job here is straightforward: You start looking for an exit. The Dalai Lama once described the job of the healer as that of leading lost strangers through the briar patch of life. The briar patch is dark and dangerous, and once you are tangled up inside it—once you have been born into this world—exits from troubles will not always be obvious. Especially for the young and inexperienced, and for others who have lost their sense of direction, the path through the briars seems to consist of nothing but blind alleys lined with flesh-tearing thorns.

But because we are therapists, because we have read all these books and have been trained to help others, we are issued a special pair of thick leather chaps. With these chaps on our legs, and armed with what we have learned about the various paths and ways through the mass of briars, we can guide others to safety. In other words, when you are working with suicidal patients whose exits are blocked, your job is to find ways over, around, and through the briar patch.

For a time, this will require that you lead and they follow. Given that your patient's problem-solving capacities are impaired to the point that he or she cannot imagine an alternative to suicide, it will be up to you to take the flashlight and start looking for another way out, a secret opening, an escape into the light. Don't worry about creating a dependent patient. Once such patients are safely on the other side of the present tangle of briars, they can learn to go forward on their own. Worry instead about keeping the person alive until a path through the briars has been found, and hope is reborn.

9. Not Approving Suicide

As I've mentioned, suicidal patients will sometimes try to persuade you that their situation truly is hopeless and that suicide is the only sensible solution. Years of psychological pain and suffering, repeated failures and losses, have left them with a deep and abiding sense of hopelessness that they are convinced will never pass. And so they are seeking professional approval for their suicide. Whether openly or obliquely, they are looking for someone in authority who will say to them, "I understand. So go ahead—it's okay to kill yourself."

If a suicidal person appears to be searching for someone in power to grant him or her permission to die, be sure you are not that someone. Never allow yourself to become an unwitting accomplice in a patient's quest for approval. Be aware that professional approval is not always overt. It can be as simple as lowering your head and letting out a sigh at the end of a long tale of woe. Or it can be as unequivocal as handing your patient a month's supply of a potentially lethal drug with the advice, "Now, George, you know if you take this all at once—especially with alcohol—it could kill you."

To avoid becoming an accomplice in a patient's suicide, make up your mind right from the start that nobody dies, everybody lives. As a healer, I make it very clear that, if I have anything to say about it, no one is going to die on my watch. So when I sense that a chronically suicidal patient is asking me to validate the conclusion that everything is indeed hopeless and, into the bargain, is requesting my permission to get it over with, I simply don't give it. This means I make every effort never to agree with patients who would argue that their psychological pain is so intractable and untreatable that they have earned my permission to stop living.

I have had suicidal patients put it to me bluntly: "Why can't I kill myself? Why won't you let me?" I tell them just as bluntly: "Because I believe you can not only survive but thrive." Another answer to someone who believes that suicide is the only option is: "I agree, something needs to die here. But it isn't you!"

When a patient is seeking approval for his or her plans to die, you will know it. In one way or another, you will sense what he or she is after. You may feel it rubbing against the grain of your life-is-worth-living wood. It may feel like a rough spot in the flow of the interview, a bump in a smooth road. You may sense it physically, as an odd feeling in your stomach, a sudden shiver, or a jump in your heart rate. Or you may feel that you are being asked to officiate at a funeral when nobody you know has died.

Pay close attention to these fleeting feelings, these gifts of tension, anxiety, or foreboding. What you are sensing may well be the person's fear—fear of the vast unknown that he or she is contemplating. Fear travels faster than thought, and more often than not it is right on target.

However you recognize this anxiety, this feeling that something bad is about to happen, trust your recognition. It could make the difference in saving a life. The intervention can be as simple as saying:

"You just said something that frightened me."
"Can you tell me more about that?"
Or, if the patient has fallen silent, "Tell me what you're thinking."

But whatever else you say or do, if a patient is saying, in effect, "Please stop fighting for me to live," don't give into the request. Remember that once the therapist has been convinced that a patient can't make it—that he or she is not worth the effort of rescue—the situation truly is hopeless. If ever you feel yourself giving up on a suicidal patient, don't delay. Turn to a supervisor or colleague and get some help.

10. Dealing with an ERA

Some suicidal people are not going to give up the means to suicide simply because you've convinced them to enter treatment. They may like you, they may take their medications and keep their appointments, but back at home in some safe place they have an ERA—an Early Retirement Account. An ERA is a suicide plan and the means to carry it out. In much the same way that an Individual Retirement Account ensures financial security in one's old age, an ERA gives the suicidal person the security of control over the end of his or her life. And, just as you would not easily give up your rainy day savings account, your pension funds, or your family's farm, neither will some suicidal people give up their capacity to control what they are convinced may be the only option for pain relief ultimately available to them.

Especially in the eyes of a seriously suicidal person, a well thought-out suicide plan can be a thing of beauty. The ERA may be something quite simple—a couple bottles of sleeping pills, a gun and a special bullet, some masking tape and a length of garden hose. It could be grandfather's old straight razor. These days, the ERA could even be some of the suicide-friendly how-to information available on the Internet.

An ERA can also be fairly elaborate. A colleague once told me about a suicidal person who had a truly impressive ERA. In addition to having had his attorney prepare a will, which provided for the distribution of his assets, he had taken care of all the death details. He had signed and posted a "no resuscitation" document over his bed in case his overdose failed and had notified a mortician to arrive at his home within two hours of his anticipated demise. Instructions were left as to who could enter the home, who was to clean up afterward, and what was to be done about the phone, the power company, and the newspaper delivery.

Sometimes the ERA represents a lifetime of thinking and planning. But the ERA can also be a recent investment, such as the purchase of an expensive .44 Magnum. But whatever it may be, the ERA is very valuable, and a seriously suicidal person is not likely just to hand it over to you simply because you asked for it. Don't expect it.

As I indicated in the chapters on intervention and assessment, when someone appears to be at imminent risk of death
and yet refuses to give up the means to suicide, you may have
little choice but to consider hospitalization. But a patient
who has an ERA is not necessarily in any immediate danger.
The ERA is the secret backup plan—the emergency exit, to be
used if and when the going gets too rough. The first step in
dealing with an ERA is therefore to discover that it exists.
This will probably require time and some gentle but persistent probing. Until a solid therapeutic alliance has been
established and the patient has come to trust you, chances are
he or she will choose to keep the ERA safely out of sight.

Even after you learn about the ERA, however, the patient
is unlikely to let go of it without a struggle. Psychologically
speaking, he or she is going to arm-wrestle you for it—not
once, but possibly every single time you meet for a therapy
session. In fact, sometimes the central preoccupation and
overriding goal of a long psychotherapeutic struggle with a
stubbornly suicidal patient is to persuade the person to give
up, finally and forever, the Early Retirement Account.

When someone is reluctant to give up an ERA, your best
option (and often your only option) is to be patient and to
continue doing therapy. As treatment progresses, and hope
is revived, the person will gradually come to see things differently—and one day he or she will decide that an Early
Retirement Account just isn't necessary.

11. The Columbo Technique

The popular television series *Columbo* featured a detec-
tive, Lieutenant Columbo, who was known for his dogged
persistence in following up the details of case. Until he was
satisfied that he understood what was going on, he never let
up in his pursuit of information. The Columbo Technique
says: Never let up until you know as much about your
patient's plans and reasons for suicide as he or she does.

While useful in many situations, the Columbo Technique is especially valuable when a patient has plans for suicide that he or she would prefer go undetected. As we have seen, people who have thought long and hard about killing themselves have often developed an elaborate suicide plan—perhaps even several such plans. They know where they will get the gun or the pills or the rope. They may have picked a time and place. They may have written several drafts of a suicide note. Yet when the therapist asks whether they have such a plan and, if so, what it consists of, the patient dismisses the question or gives only a brief, uninformative reply.

People who have been careful and methodical in the living of life are likely to be careful and methodical in carrying out an act of suicide. Especially from such people, you should never accept vague, evasive, or incomplete answers to your questions about plans for suicide. But rather than demanding a full account early on, which could put a burgeoning therapeutic alliance at risk, you would do better to come back to the same question again. And again. And again. Or put the same question in a slightly different way. For example:

> *Therapist:* You said you were going to use a gun. . . . Is that your gun, or someone else's?
> *Patient:* What difference does it make?
> *Therapist:* Oh, none, I suppose. I was just wondering. Maybe your friend wouldn't give it to you if he knew what you were going to do with it.
> *Patient:* He's not a friend, he's my brother, and he would, too. He knows me and he respects me. If he knew I was going to kill myself, he'd let me do it.
> *Therapist:* Is your brother's gun a .38 or a .22?
> *Patient* (growing testy): Why are you so interested in my brother's gun?

Therapist: Does it come with bullets? Hollow points, or just soft-nosed rounds?

Patient: I don't know what kind. And, hey, this is *my* business.

But it isn't his business, not now that he's sitting in your office or you are sitting in his home on a professional visit. And, thanks to the Columbo Technique, you now know several things you wouldn't have known if you'd allowed the patient to put you off. You know whose weapon it is and that it probably comes with bullets. You also know that your patient has a brother who respects him and so might be of help in saving a life.

I once had the occasion to review the completed suicide of a clinically depressed older man who was facing unwanted surgery. Reluctantly, he had acknowledged to a social worker that he was planning to use a pistol to kill himself. But then, when the social worker asked whether he would give up the pistol, he agreed quite readily. He went to a closet and handed over the gun. The next day he shot himself with another pistol. We will obviously never know whether intense curiosity and a few further questions—"Is this the pistol you planned to use?" and "Do you have any other firearms in the house?"—might have resulted in a confrontation that could have led to hospitalization and lifesaving treatment.

This is not to blame the social worker, who acted very responsibly. The lesson to take is that seriously suicidal people, people who firmly believe that death is the only answer, are unlikely to be deterred from following through on their plans unless the healer takes a persistent, even dogged approach to the assessment of risk. Curiosity kills cats, not therapists, and intense curiosity may save a life.

12. Monkey Wrenching

Much like the wedge-driving questions outlined earlier,

cognitive monkey wrenching is a way to invade and then disrupt a patient's suicidal thoughts and plans. In this case, you do so by putting yourself right in the middle of them. Being intensely curious helps make this possible.

For at least some suicidal sufferers, suicidal ideation is more a friend than an enemy. It is the one place they can go where they still feel some sense of control—even relief. Allow a therapist into the middle of these calming reflections, this chapel of peaceful flirtation with death, and that place of respite will never be the same again. In short, cognitive monkey wrenching is a way to desanctify the church in which the image of death is worshiped.

To throw a monkey wrench into the works, you begin by gently prying into the patient's private world with questions about the details of their experience with suicidal thoughts and feelings—how they envisage their suicide, what means they would choose, what place they would select, how they feel when they think about it, what fantasies they have about the reactions of others, and so on. Once you know as much about the shape, color, smell, and texture of the patient's thoughts as he or she does, it is usually quite easy to toss a wrench into the works. Here are a few wrenches that worked for me.

"Hmm. The next time you're down by the river looking at the water and imagining what a relief it would be to slip quietly under the ripples, I wonder whether you'll hear my voice right behind you, asking, 'Are you sure this is such a good idea?'" The patient's once-perfect fantasy of suicide has just had a monkey wrench tossed into it. Plan A, jumping into the river, is never going to be quite the same again.

"You know how you like to sit and stare into the candles just before you take out that little razor you keep in the drawer by your bed to make cuts on your wrists? Well, I hope my face doesn't mysteriously start to appear in the flames." The patient's self-hypnotic induction into an episode of life-threatening behavior, and the comfort she derived from the warm blood flowing over her arms, is no longer a private party. A gate crasher has ruined everything.

You know you've jammed things up if the patient gets upset with you. People who find relief in thinking about suicide don't generally like you or anyone else mucking around in their reveries. These are, like garden paths and quiet pools, mental retreats that provide respite from the otherwise seamless suffering of their lives. Not a few of my patients have become visibly angry right after they realized that my presence was going to intrude the next time they started thinking about killing themselves. But that's okay. People get over anger. It's death that's not so easy to undo.

One teenage boy I worked with used to lie on his bed in the evening listening to songs about suicide and tickling his chest over his heart with a needle-sharp bayonet, all the time wondering how quickly his heart would stop beating if he sliced it in half. In our second session, we engaged in a long, detailed exploration of this behavior, and I suggested that perhaps together we could find other ways for him to entertain himself. In the very next session he told me, "It doesn't work anymore . . . the knife thing, I mean. I tried it once, and all I could think about was what we talked about last time."

This depressed kid and his family needed and got family therapy. The parents eventually divorced, and their talented young son went on to college, majoring in art. When I asked him, at one point, whether he would copy down the lyrics from one of his favorite suicide songs before our next session, he said, "Got a pencil?" Then, without a pause, he dictated the lines to Helix's "Deep Cuts the Knife" to me from memory. I still have the lyrics, and I even remember a line or two—which just goes to show that patients can do a bit of cognitive monkey wrenching, too.

13. Permission to Live

However it comes about psychologically, some suicidal people feel they are obligated to die. They may believe that certain standards exist and that, by the light of these standards, they no longer have a right to go on living. Down through history, and in many different societies, the creed of "death before dishonor" has resulted in innumerable civilian and military suicides. Even today, cultures exist in which women who have been raped are expected to kill themselves, and often do.

But if we now view the notion of obligatory suicide as a relic of the past, it is well to remember that one of the more common messages heard from suicidal people is that they don't want to be a burden on others. Because they are financially and emotionally dependent on others, children and adolescents are especially vulnerable to such feelings, and so are the elderly. Under some circumstances, they may come to believe that their death would be a release for others—that suicide is the only responsible solution to someone else's problems.

Of course, no one has the right to expect another person to kill himself or herself in order to solve a problem, be it social, psychological, or economic. However, whether consciously or unconsciously, people do sometimes wish for another's death, and a sensitive soul can pick up on that wish. Then again, the suicidal person may have drawn the wrong conclusions from the evidence available. Either way, though, the patient's conviction that his or her death would unburden someone else is very real.

Here are several ways to explore such a belief and convey to a suicidal patient that he or she is under no obligation to die:

"Who would like you to die?"
"Is it written down somewhere that you have an
    obligation to die?"

"Where did you get the idea that when something like this happens, you're supposed to kill yourself?"

You can also counter the belief with affirmations such as:

"I want you to know, in no uncertain terms, that it's okay with me if you live. In fact, you have my unqualified permission."
"No one has the right to expect you to end your life just so theirs can be easier."
"I don't know about anybody else, but I want you to live. What's more, I insist on it."

Here is one situation in which your authority as the healer and therapist is invaluable. It gives you the power to override the messages that suicidal patients have been hearing from others, or from themselves. For suicidal people of all ages, but especially the young and the old, granting permission to live can be life saving. The effect, when I've personally seen it take hold, is often like that of handing a reprieve to someone who is expecting to be hanged on the morrow.

14. Permission to Say the Unsayable

It is always worth considering the possibility that the suicidal person in front of you has never been able to, or felt allowed to, express the full range of his or her emotions or to talk about certain aspects of his or her thoughts, particularly those that seem unspeakably ugly. Part of what we do in therapy is to name and normalize what the sufferer believes should not be named and is abnormal. What is nameless produces fear. What is thought to be abnormal produces shame.

In order to reduce anxiety, fear, and shame, we sometimes need to give a patient permission, implicitly and/or explicitly, to say what he or she has already thought and to voice what he or she has already felt—like wanting to kill your husband, for example. Or wishing your whole family would die in a fiery crash. Or being afraid that if you start crying you will never be able to stop. Or it may be that patients have done things they regard as so reprehensible or so disgusting that they live in fear of what others would think if they knew. But if dark secrets and "unacceptable" thoughts and feelings are ever to be examined in the light of common human understanding, they first need to be shared. And sharing them is usually only possible in an atmosphere of support and trust.

It helps if you're not easily shocked, or even much surprised, by the full range of human behavior, no matter how offensive or bizarre. If you do find yourself stunned, or appalled, by some unusual revelation, try not to overreact. Whatever your private feelings, you must guard against conveying a message that would essentially confirm the patient's worst fears and thus add to, rather than reduce, the person's already heavy load of shame and self-recrimination. If you do, your patient will almost invariably retreat from the session, quickly putting the cork back into the bottle in which unspeakable thoughts and feelings have been so carefully hidden. Rather, the goal is to bring secrets into the open and allow the patient to discover that, strange though it may seem, others have thought and felt and done equally "abnormal" things. The more experience you have as a therapist, the easier this will be to do.

15. Family Entanglements

Suicide almost always involves significant others. Sometimes the suicidal person is striking back at loved ones for abuse received or rejection perceived. Others are entangled in dysfunctional family systems and are clinging to intricate, long-standing pathological patterns from which death seems the only means of escape. There may be all sorts of dark struggles going on among the players, in which the patient is deeply enmeshed. Or there may be shameful family secrets, as well as firm prohibitions against anyone stepping outside of the family system for help. Given that suicide would solve, quite permanently, all the patient's problems—enmeshment issues, conflicted communications with parents or parental figures, separation anxieties, fear of abandonment, and so on—the thought of exiting a sick family via suicide can be very tempting.

In working with suicidal children (and a person of any age who is still living in the home can be considered a child), ask yourself what would happen to the parents if this child grew up and left. If terrible consequences would ensue—the parents would probably divorce, the mother would sicken and die, the father would lose the only child who defends him against his wife—then you know, right off, that family therapy is indicated. The family's chief task is to raise its offspring into healthy, autonomous adults, and its failure to do so is a signal that something is very wrong. Growing up shouldn't be a form of disloyalty. It shouldn't mean abandoning your mother to an abusive husband or condemning your father to intolerable loneliness or otherwise putting a family member in some sort of physical or emotional jeopardy.

This is not the place to detail the ins and outs of good family systems therapy. But if you are working with someone who is clearly struggling with family pathology, you must at least understand precisely how your patient's wish to die fits into the family belief structure and what consequences his or her suicide would have for others. Dysfunctional family systems often include an identified patient—the person who has volunteered (usually unconsciously) or been asked (usually wordlessly) to assume the burden of illness. To deal only with the identified patient in such systems is to significantly limit your effectiveness and thus your ability to lower the risk of suicide.

If there really is no other option, you will have to work with the identified patient alone, and this is certainly possible, even if it is not ideal. But when your clinical judgment tells you that your patient's suicidal impulses are grounded in broader family issues, your best option is to get everyone together, have them make a commitment to keep everyone in the family safe, and then set the ground rules for how the therapy will proceed. If you've already had experience with family therapy, you know what to do. If you're not, bring in a trained family therapist or get some training for yourself.

16. Removing Parents

The vast majority of parents of suicidal children do love them. They may not understand the nature and the dangers of depression or other psychiatric disorders, but they love their children. Sadly, though, it is also true that some parents do not love their children. As difficult as it might be to believe, some parents openly wish their children were dead. Many more keep such wishes to themselves but express the desire indirectly, by reinforcing, whether consciously or unconsciously, self-destructive behavior on the part of a child. They may even encourage a child's suicide, if not in so many words then in deeds—for example, by giving a depressed, anxiety-ridden teenager facing school and relationship failures a hunting rifle for his birthday.

Kids are especially smart about relationships and can sense rejection across a crowded room. Sometimes the impressions they gather are wrong, but sometimes they're right. When we are working with youth, we cannot afford to take chances by automatically siding with the parents' version (or versions) of a family's reality. Parents who hate their children can actually kill them—and suicide conveniently shifts the blame to the victim.

I remember once making observations such as these during a discussion of suicide on a television talk show in Los Angeles. The moderator challenged me: "Doctor, are you saying that some parents actually encourage their children to suicide?" I said yes.

Sitting next to me was a Catholic priest who worked with troubled and suicidal teens. The moderator turned to him and asked, "That can't be true, can it, Father?"

"Oh, it's true all right," the priest replied. "We wish it weren't true, but it happens all the time."

Consider just the following possibilities. Could it be that the child in front of you:

- Was unwanted?
- Is causing problems for a lover?
- Was fathered by someone other than the man the child believes is his or her father and that one or both parents know this?
- Poses an economic burden to the family??
- Has a parent who is mentally ill and is convinced that the child is cursed or possessed by a demon? Strongly resembles a much-hated parent or family member?
- Is creating problems for another, more loved child in the family?
- Is being raised by people who are pathologically insensitive to psychological pain and suffering?
- Has been designated by the family as the "problem kid," from whom nothing good can ever be expected?

Obviously, no child should have to die to solve a parent's problems. This is another of those times when we need to be bold. We need to take off our blinders and let go of the comforting illusion that all parents deeply love and respect their offspring. Instead, we need to learn everything we can about the family's history, dynamics, rituals, beliefs, and expectations.

Once you have determined that a child may be acting out the desires of parents who are terribly troubled, it is essential that you evaluate the entire family system and take whatever steps may be necessary to safeguard the child from harm. Removing sick and suicidogenic parents from a child's life is not an operation to be undertaken by the inexperienced or unskilled. Still, performing a "parentectomy" can be a lifesaving intervention. Sometimes the only way to guarantee a child's safety is to remove the parents from the child's life—if not physically, then psychologically, through counseling and therapy.

To remove a parent or parents you will need the help of a child welfare agency and perhaps a clergyman, a physician, and/or a whole team of mental health professionals. There are authorities who can assist you and laws that will protect your actions on behalf of an at-risk child. Learn what these laws are and do not hesitate to turn to them when you need them.

17. Unlearning Shame

Particularly when you have encouraged patients to express their innermost thoughts and feelings, it is critical that you keep shame at arm's length. This is especially important in the case of adolescents and adults who were raised in shame-based families. Feelings of worthlessness and an abiding sense of humiliation can often be traced to a parent or parents whose techniques of child management were founded on the notion that a properly shamed child is a properly behaved one. Some parents are able to instill feelings of shame in a child almost as if they were skilled hypnotists making posthypnotic suggestions. Their children are taught shame before they've even developed much by way of language skills, let alone any self-esteem or the ability to fight back.

A lingering sense of shame is often a driving force behind the impulse to suicide. A person who has internalized the message that he or she is a deeply undeserving human being will often plan a very proper suicide. The plan will be discreet and tidy, and all due attention will have been paid to matters of propriety—to the appearance of the corpse, to ensuring that personal affairs and household matters are in order, to the details of funeral arrangements, and so on. People who have grown up believing that they are fundamentally flawed human beings will tend to be at pains to avoid inconveniencing others by their death.

Even intelligent and successful adults can be trapped in a legacy of shame. I once worked with a physician raised by a cold and distant father who evidently suspected that his son was basically "a dirty and worthless little bastard." One of his main messages was, "Don't you ever dare to do anything that might bring shame to this family." And so there was never really any question in this man's mind that sooner or later he would have to kill himself. Undoing this curse by investigating the roots of the shame he experienced as a boy was the central part of his therapy. Helping patients such as this man understand and accept that, as the poet said, we come through our parents, not from them, can be life saving.

It makes good sense, then, that when you are working with patients who are terribly burdened by shame, you must be careful not to allow even a whisper of condemnation to escape your own lips or to behave in a way that might suggest disapproval. Our job is not to judge but to root out potentially lethal feelings of shame, lay them on a heavy table in a good light, and smash them into harmless pieces.

Be advised, however, that it usually does little good to make a frontal assault on the shaming parent, especially if the parent is still alive, lives in the same town, or is sitting out in the waiting room. Blood is thicker than water—at least at the beginning of therapy. It is your gentle questioning, your unstinting support, and your understanding of the process of separation and individuation that will, over time, lead to a change in self-perception and foster the development of enough self-esteem that your patient will finally be able to separate successfully from his or her parents.

18. Reframing

Sometimes a person who is suicidal doesn't actually want to die. What the person really wants is more power over a problem or an unpleasant set of circumstances, and suicide seems like the obvious solution. In such situations, a technique known as reframing can prove very valuable.

The point of reframing is to translate the overt wish to die into the underlying wish for greater control. For example:

Situation: A young woman says she wants to kill herself because her boyfriend is leaving her.

Reframing: "It sounds like you're very angry at him and don't want to be left all alone."

Situation: A man is feeling suicidal because his business is failing and his wife just told him she wants a divorce.

Reframing: "If you could save the business, would you still need to die? Or suppose your wife were to come back. Then you'd feel more in control of things, wouldn't you, and you could work on getting the business back on its feet."

Situation: A teenage boy has just been arrested for shoplifting. He's failing in school and now he's been suspended. Already depressed and miserable and frightened, he says he would rather die than face his father.

Reframing: "I can understand why you're afraid your father will punish you. If you felt a little stronger and knew better how he might handle this, would you feel less frightened about what may happen?"

Reframing helps the patient to see that suicide is an escapist response to a situation that feels awful and uncontrollable. The goal is to convince the patient that, if the need for greater control is the real problem, then suicide truly is a false solution. Repeatedly prompting the patient to acknowledge the wish for more control can gradually reorient the person's thinking and thus lead to better problem solving.

Because such patients don't want to die so much as gain power over people and circumstances, they are somewhat less at risk than patients who are struggling with an overwhelming sense of utter hopelessness. But this is not to say that people don't kill themselves in a misguided effort to influence others or get out of a mess they're in. They do. And in a way motivations for suicide that involve an underlying desire for control are among our most challenging. To help such patients we need the usual working alliance, solid therapeutic boundaries, and many of the tools and techniques outlined in this book.

19. Times of Increased Risk

Over the sometimes long haul of therapy, it is likely that events—both planned and unplanned—will occur that increase the patient's level of stress and hence his or her vulnerability to thoughts of suicide. These are often developing situations over which the patient feels he or she has increasingly less control, or none at all. Anticipate these windows of risk, bring them into the therapy, and be prepared to manage them aggressively. A partial list of such risks would include:

- The final realization that an important and cherished relationship has truly ended
- The return of a psychiatric illness in acute form
- The suicide of someone the patient knows
- The death of a loved one (particularly if the person dies by suicide)
- The anniversary of some major loss
- The onset of serious physical illness
- Any seriously traumatic event, such as a rape or a disabling and/or disfiguring injury
- The loss of a job, especially one that gave the person a sense of identity and self-worth
- The unwanted ending of a treatment relationship, for whatever reason
- Any return to drinking or drug use, even if only an isolated episode
- The completion of an drug or alcohol treatment program, especially an inpatient one. To someone who is new to recovery, the world can suddenly seem a very cold and frightening place. Worse yet, all the problems that the addiction kept at a distance are still there to be solved.
- Discharge from a psychiatric hospital
- Any loss, real or imagined, that the patient perceives to be unacceptable.

The wise therapist anticipates as many of the slings and arrows of outrageous fortune as possible and tries to prepare the patient to cope with them, as well as offering support and guidance during such events and in their immediate aftermath. This may entail scheduling extra sessions or calling on outside support. It is often valuable to begin by asking a patient to think about what could happen in the future that might provoke renewed suicidal feelings. Talking these possibilities through can make them seem more like known quantities and therefore less frightening. Likewise, discussing what the two of you will do if and when a dreaded event occurs can help to reduce anxiety and thus safeguard the patient against another suicidal crisis.

20. The Calm Before the Storm

As is well known, suicidal people often feel a wonderful sense of relief when finally they decide, once and for all, to kill themselves. They have been engaged in a life-and-death struggle before their own mental jury, and at long last the verdict is in. Even though the sentence is death, the case is now closed, and their tribulations are behind them. Beware the suddenly peaceful patient!

The decision to die lifts a great burden from the shoulders of the sufferer. After the decision has been made, a beatific, Buddha-like smile may appear on the suicidal person's face. You may find yourself wondering, *Why is this person suddenly so at peace? What has truly changed? Has the medication magically kicked in . . . or is this a decision to die?* Indeed, to the therapist whose patient has been battling with the choice of living or dying, this smile—this sudden chipperness, this abrupt change in the weather, this overnight shift from misery to peace, this miraculous cure—should sound a five-alarm fire bell.

Having read the final entries in the medical records of a number of patients who killed themselves shortly after their last outpatient visit, I can assure you that observations such as "Seems much better today" or "Mood much improved, patient doing well" come to seem almost predictable. Consider the following:

A depressed, suicidal young professional woman who was recently fired from a much-loved job throws a party for her closest friends the day after her discharge from a psychiatric hospital. That night she dies of a massive overdose. *Where there is no real cause, why is there a celebration?*

A middle-aged man seeks therapy for depression but denies his alcoholism. His marriage is failing, his job is in jeopardy, and his children won't speak to him. He expects to be laid off from work at the end of the week, but on Thursday he tells his therapist that he's come into some unexpected money and seems "almost jovial." He shoots himself in the head with a shotgun two days later. *Unexpected expressions of joy are suspicious and must be explored.*

A woman who for the past two decades has suffered from chronic pain and depression announces to her physician that she no longer needs her antidepressant medication and has stopped taking it. She appears in an upbeat mood. A devout Catholic, she tells her doctor, "There's nothing to worry about now. . . . I've seen the Virgin." She returns home and shoots herself in the head with her husband's .38-caliber pistol. *Where the medicine is not working, there should be no cure.*

The work of therapy is seldom easy for anyone, let alone suicidal people. Sometimes, after weeks or even months of long, difficult, and seemingly unproductive therapeutic efforts, and the failure of one medication after another, the patient will decide to give up the struggle without letting you know. But because the patient feels that courtesy is owed, he or she will keep one last appointment. Or make one last call to cancel. It is during this appointment or phone conversation that the patient's mood may appear so much improved.

When you are working with someone who is suicidal, this is the time to hit the panic button, and hit it immediately. Ask the person:

"You look awfully happy today. Can you tell me why?"
"Yesterday you were miserable, and today you seem so
    calm. Do you know something I don't?"
"Have you made up your mind to kill yourself?"

The best place to ask these questions is in the office, but if you first detect this strange calm over the phone, ask over the phone. But wherever you ask, and whatever else you do, you must restore the therapeutic alliance. You must persuade the patient to talk about what is going on and to reaffirm a commitment to safety and ongoing treatment.

21. Back to the Couch

This intervention was taught to me by a chronically suicidal patient I once treated. She invariably waited until the end of the therapy hour to let me know she was going to leave my office, go home, and kill herself. She had several roundabout ways of communicating this. One of my favorites was, "You've been awfully kind to me these past months. I'll call and schedule another appointment sometime next week."

This was a lie. We had a standing appointment. She had no intention of calling me. Her smile and apparently much brightened mood was—excuse the pun—a dead giveaway. What she was really saying was, "Thanks for trying, but I've decided to go ahead and get it over with."

On receiving this message, I would march her back to the couch, and we would start in all over again. My next patient might have to wait, but this one wasn't leaving until she was feeling properly miserable again—miserable, but recommitted to therapy, at least for another week.

22. Rewriting the Script

In working with someone suicidal, one of your first tasks will be to discover just where he or she got the idea that suicide is an acceptable solution to life's problems. The previously unexamined belief that, under certain circumstances, killing yourself is a reasonable option—or perhaps the only option—must be traced to its very source. Once the foundations of this belief have been laid bare, the belief can be challenged, chipped away at, assaulted, disassembled, and otherwise undermined.

The idea that "If things don't work out, I can always kill myself" does not materialize out of thin air. It has been learned. Most often, it has been learned directly from another human being—a parent or other relative, or perhaps a friend. Then again the source could be a movie or book or someone the patient has heard about but never met. And, as we have seen, the idea that suicide is acceptable can even be embedded in culture. It was tradition that taught a samurai warrior what he was obliged to do should he ever be disgraced.

Some suicidal people, however, don't merely believe that suicide is a viable option. They believe that their suicide is somehow inevitable—that they are destined to die by their own hand. Ernest Hemingway's father, for example, scripted his son to suicide by shooting himself while Hemingway was still a youth. The themes of death and suicide haunted the writer all his days, and we can only hope that the legacy of Hemingway suicides ended with that of his granddaughter Margaux.

Locating the psychological source of the conviction that one's suicide is essentially a foregone conclusion will probably include identifying a role model for suicide. But pinpointing the source is critical to undoing the influence of that belief. Unless this fatal setup is dismantled, healing may prove very difficult, even impossible. Here is one useful intervention:

- ◆ Introduce the analogy that life is like a three-act play. Ask the patient where we are in the play as we sit together and talk. Act I, scene 2? Act III, scene 3?
- ◆ Confirm that, as matters presently stand, this play of life is closer to a tragedy than a comedy.

Then ask whether the play started out as a tragedy or whether the plot changed along the way. If it changed, when did it change, and why?

+ Ask the patient who is writing the script for the play. Is it the patient? The patient's mother or father? And who wrote into the script the scene where the patient dies by suicide?

The answer to these questions should tell you who set the stage for tragedy and who wrote the first draft of the suicide script. Then, not only must the script itself be called into question, but the right of its original author to cast the patient in the role of suicide victim must be challenged.

Too commonly, as in the case of Hemingway, the script's author is a parent who died by suicide. A patient will often feel protective of this long-deceased parent and may at first react defensively to your attempts to probe the past. You may be told that you should allow the dead to rest in peace rather than dig them up and begin attacking them for the psychological legacy they bequeathed to those they left behind. But that's exactly what you must do. Regardless of how the patient came by the script, the belief that he or she must one day die by suicide is just that: a belief. A belief is not a reality until you act on it. Nothing is destined. Death by suicide is never a requirement, no matter who wrote the script.

Fortunately, the strength with which our beliefs are held is not fixed. Early on in counseling, those scripted to die by suicide may be quite firmly convinced that they will someday die by their own hand. As therapy progresses, however, the belief that they might instead die of natural causes at the close of a long and relatively happy life begins to gain strength, and the belief in an early death by suicide weakens accordingly.

Even so, the conviction that suicide is both acceptable and inevitable can be remarkably tenacious. I have had a patient's belief in life appear to increase dramatically only to hear the person later say, "Well, things are going all right now, but if she leaves me again, I'll have to kill myself." When this happens, it is clear that the core of the belief is still firm, which means that work remains to be done.

To help a suicidal patient revise a deeply rooted belief in the inevitability of his or her suicide you will need to help the patient rewrite his or her own life script, often from the very beginning. Such a process can be empowering, but it can also be frightening. Many patients have never seen themselves as the author of their own lives. Getting any-one—let alone a depressed and suicidal person—to assume this awesome responsibility, teaching them to take charge of their destiny, is seldom easy. You must work at it, and your patient must be willing to work with you. But once the process takes hold, the growth of a patient's sense of per-sonal control over his or her own life can be amazing. Once those scripted to suicide realize that death by their own hand is never foreordained—one they realize that, at the very worst, someone could murder them—then the heavy cloud of impending doom lifts, and the future is suddenly filled with possibilities.

23. Imaging After Death

This technique is one to be approached with some cau-tion, and only when you are absolutely sure you have a firm therapeutic alliance with your patient. When I have used this intervention, I have done so because other methods of countering the patient's desire to die were not working. Used carefully, it is a technique that can pay big dividends. It can help you to evaluate how clearly (or not) a suicidal person is thinking and to what extent anger, the desire for revenge, and/or sheer impulse are driving the wish to die.

The technique involves asking a series of questions that push patients beyond the act of suicide itself and require them to imagine what the future will look like without them in it. Such questions might include the following:

If you kill yourself, who will find your body? The answer to this question may reveal that the patient is hoping to wound someone by his or her death—that some specific person (usually one with whom the patient is angry) is supposed to have the shock of discovering the corpse.

Who will attend your funeral, and how will they feel? This question helps you to identify key people in the patient's life and discover how the patient imagines they will respond to his or her death.

What will happen to those you love once you are gone? This obliges the patient to imagine the reactions of those left behind and to consider what the future will be like for them.

What is the legacy you wish to leave to those who knew you? Learning whether the patient has specific gifts that he or she wishes to bestow—or withhold—again provides information about the patient's feelings toward important others in his or her life and about how the person wishes to be remembered.

If you have not written your will, how will it read? Similarly, this question can point to relationship problems and thus help you understand the interpersonal dynamics at work in the patient's life (and plans for death).

As a therapeutic strategy, posing such questions has a number of advantages:

- ◆ The patient is brought up close to the finality of death. Pushing a patient to look at the details, to confront the reality of what he or she is contemplating, can work to undermine the patient's escapist fantasies. This can be especially helpful when you are working with an adolescent or teenager.

- The patient is forced to examine his or her true motives for suicide. To hurt others? To unburden significant others? To avoid some terrible shame or confrontation?
- Imagining the lives of friends and family well past the funeral can help a patient recognize that, in the longer scheme of life, the current crisis is only a temporary circumstance—whereas death is very permanent.

If the suicidal person has difficulty coming up with answers to your questions, it may be that the person's thinking is more severely impaired than you initially thought. Seriously depressed people tend to suffer from tunnel vision, which can lead them to believe that suicide is their best, or their only, option.

The tunnel vision that so often accompanies the journey to suicide is memorably illustrated in the Christmas classic *It's a Wonderful Life*—required viewing each holiday season in America. In this story, George Bailey (Jimmy Stewart) is faced with the unacceptable and personally humiliating loss of an investor's funds, for which he is wrongly blamed. Realizing that his business will be forced into bankruptcy and that he will be sent to jail, he becomes frightened and angry. He goes to a bar, drinks too much, and eventually winds up on a bridge, where he resolves to jump to his death. In his agitated and intoxicated state, he believes that suicide will solve his problems. It will allow him to avoid public humiliation, and his wife and children will have the money from his life insurance. His thinking stops there: He can't see any farther into the future.

But fate intervenes in the form of an angel named Clarence, who jumps into the river himself, thereby obligating George to save him. Clarence then shows George what would have happened if, instead, he had been the one to jump. He painfully learns that, had he perished, all the people he most cared about would have ended up in misery, and the greedy bank owner, Mr. Potter, would have succeeded in gaining control of the town, renaming it "Pottersville," and reducing it to a slum.

This may be the stuff of Hollywood, but it is also the stuff of therapy. Caught in the press of the problems facing them, suicidal people focus on the immediate relief that death would provide, not on the consequences for others of that death. In their depressed condition, they have only a limited capacity to envisage future scenarios or to appreciate the part they play in other people's lives.

In truth, survivors of suicide are often furious at the deceased loved one, whom they accuse of being "selfish" or "thoughtless." In a way, these words are apt. But if in choosing to die their loved one acted selfishly and thoughtlessly, it was probably not so much out of a basic insensitivity to the needs of others. More likely, the person's ability to think clearly and critically and to imagine alternative solutions to his or her problems was crippled by severe depression, possibly coupled with intoxication. He or she could not see far enough beyond the act of suicide itself to imagine with any accuracy what it would mean.

24. Revenge Suicide

Pushing a patient to spin a death-and-consequences scenario sometimes reveals that the desire to die is very much about inflicting psychological pain on others. Called a revenge suicide, such an act is motivated by a desire to strike back, to hurt others as the patient believes he or she has been hurt. Sometimes the perception of having been gravely injured by others is quite accurate. More often, though, there is relatively little reality to support it. As we know, impaired thinking, with its distortions and wrong conclusions, is a hallmark of serious depression.

If you learn that the desire to retaliate is a significant part of a sufferer's motivation for suicide, you will need to work on reframing this desire. The desire for revenge may be rooted in a need for more control, a need for more love and attention from others, or a need to be heard and understood. By shifting the focus to underlying needs and wishes, reframing allows the suicidal person to view his or her situation in a new and more realistic light.

Ironically enough, however, far from being rooted in a desire for revenge, sometimes the wish to die is grounded in what the suicidal person sees as altruistic motives. Especially for a patient who feels that he or she is fundamentally a burden to others, suicide is intended to make life easier for the survivors, not harder. In reality, however, this conclusion is almost always inaccurate.

I once treated a suicidal patient who, before killing himself, was planning to sell his business and make arrangements with an attorney so that the money from the sale would be used to take care of his three children, ages four, seven, and nine. (His wife, he told me, could "Go suck an egg.") I knew that this man deeply loved his children, but I also knew that he was far from a multimillionaire. And so I challenged him to do the math to support his goodwill gesture—not later, at home, but right there in my office, right this minute. I handed him a pocket calculator. Would he be leaving his children with enough money to see them through a college education? Hardly. After we'd crunched the numbers, the truth shocked him. The money wouldn't suffice to get them out of high school, let alone college. This hard fact brought him up short and enabled us to work toward a more effective solution to his problems.

Even though his future included an ugly divorce and a long road to recovery from alcoholism, this once suicidally depressed man eventually ended up not only building a successful business but winning full custody of his children.

I've run into him several times since we worked together, once when he was coming out of a theater with two of his children, now teenagers. He introduced his kids to me and told them, "This man helped me a long time ago." It is rewards like this that keep a therapist going.

Consider also a parent who says, "The kids would be better off without me." One can challenge this distorted perception head on, simply by reminding the person that such a conclusion is not true and will never be true. Even the most flawed parent has value. When we are depressed, we are naturally prone to see only our shortcomings—but this is a problem with our vision, not our reality. Moreover, when parents kill themselves, not only do they leave a psychological curse as a legacy to their children, but they also duck out on their very real emotional, psychological, social, and financial responsibilities to help their children grow up, finish school, and make their way in the world.

Making such an argument may seem too harsh, too guilt inducing, and hence too risky an approach to take with someone who is already seriously depressed. But when nothing else is working, grounding a patient in future reality can be a powerful means of demonstrating that suicide is a false solution. I have not generally found that fear of the hereafter, or of God's anger, or of the possibility that death is unending nothingness to be much of a deterrent to suicide. If anything, it is their responsibilities on this side of the grave that help keep people alive—a fact I am not above using if I need to get someone's attention.

Sadly, though, sometimes a patient's conclusion that his or her suicide would make things easier for others is all too correct. If you ask a patient to imagine what the future will look like after he or she is dead and discover that nobody in fact wants this person around, you have obviously learned something extremely important. But you will need to get to work right away at bringing about a fundamental change in the patient's environment, both social and psychological, and in the patient's self-perception. Your job will be to guide the person to the conviction that, no matter what, he or she is a worthwhile human being who deserves something better than death.

25. Socratic Dialogues

One of the most useful tools for a therapist who is grappling with the negative, distorted, and confused cognitions of a suicidal person is the Socratic dialogue: the method of teaching by posing a series of questions that lead the student to a new understanding. Rather than tell his students what to think, Socrates simply asked them questions until they uncovered some truth or other for themselves. Ask enough good questions and, sooner or later, the suicidal person will be drawn to a conclusion other than self-inflicted death.

Consider a situation in which a man is being left by a woman he doesn't want to lose. Here is how such a dialogue might proceed:

>*Therapist:* Why do you think she rejected you?
>*Patient:* They always reject me. Didn't I tell you that?
>   I'm selfish and stupid.
>*Therapist:* Have you always been selfish and stupid?
>*Patient:* Yes.
>*Therapist:* With everyone, or only with women?
>*Patient:* Hmmm. Maybe more with women.
>*Therapist: Maybe* more with women?
>*Patient:* Well, once in a while I can be pretty generous.
>*Therapist:* Like when?
>*Patient:* I once gave an old fiancée an expensive diamond.
>*Therapist:* What happened to her?
>*Patient:* It didn't work out. I found somebody else.
>*Therapist:* What happened to the ring?

Patient: I let her keep it. I'm not stingy.

Therapist: Let me get this straight. *You* left her, she didn't leave you? And you let her keep the ring?

Patient: Yes.

Therapist: And you didn't become suicidal?

Patient: No, why should I? I was leaving her.

Therapist: Then women don't always reject you. In fact, sometimes *you* reject women?

Patient: Say . . . are you trying to trip me up, or what?

Depending on the quality of the therapeutic relationship, the therapist might now say something like, "You old heartbreaker, you. You've left a few, haven't you? And being a big-hearted guy, you let the last one keep the ring? Am I right?"

Socrates would wait for an answer, and so should you. Prompted by the therapist's questions, the patient was able to discover a few small truths on his own. He learned that:

- Women do not always leave him.
- He is not a perfectly rejectable person.
- He is not always selfish and stupid.

The purpose of such questioning is to reveal the distorted "facts" and the inconsistencies in reasoning based on these false facts that in turn lead to false conclusions. According to the categorical and rigid thinking of depressed persons, if you are *always* rejected because you are *always* selfish and stupid and can *never* make *any* relationship work with *any* woman, well, then, you are a hopeless case. And if you are a hopeless case, then you *ought* to do the decent thing and just shoot yourself. The truth, however, is not black or white, not something *always* or *never*. Our man has been hurt, but the wound is not fatal. He does not *have* to die. He may need to grow up a little—but die, no.

This approach owes its origins not only to the Greek philosopher but also to one of his students, Albert Ellis. Socratic questioning is one of the techniques outlined in *Rational Emotive Behavior Therapy* (Ellis and MacLaren 2005). Here are three keys to getting good results with this method:

- Never embarrass the person you're questioning. In all likelihood, he or she is already struggling with feelings of confusion and worthlessness, so keep shame at bay. Keep your questions straightforward, logical, progressive, and friendly.
- Be patient. Let the person draw his or her own conclusions from your questions. These self-discoveries are much more valuable to a patient than any lecture you might be tempted to deliver. Moreover, making these discoveries increases the sufferer's self-esteem—something you may have in abundance but of which the suicidal person has little.
- Each time the patient draws a new conclusion and makes some sort of positive, life-affirming statement, jot it down in your notes, put quotation marks around it, and then circle it. Later, when the patient is again mired in misery and low self-esteem, you can read back something you recorded earlier.

For example, the patient may say: "Maybe I don't always get my facts straight, but I'm really not such a bad person." Or, "People used to really like me before I met Christy. . . . Maybe she changed me for the worse." Or, "I guess I forget about them, but actually I have done a few good things with my life."

To combat the logic that so relentlessly argues the case for death by suicide and to improve the patient's chances for survival, you need all the positive self-statements you can extract from the person. Repeatedly returning to such statements over the course of therapy can give the patient strength in the same way that a well-considered compliment makes people genuinely feel good about themselves. More important, such self-affirmations will help the patient slowly restore a positive self-image—and people who value themselves choose life, not death.

Socrates might say to the patient, "So now we know you're basically a decent, thoughtful, caring human being who only occasionally draws wrong conclusions from questionable facts. Tell me, then. Does it make sense to put such a person to death?"

26. False Pride

Ending one's own life can be a matter of honor or pride, a way to safeguard one's reputation or avoid some personally humiliating event. History is strewn with lives self-sacrificed on the altar of honor. One can understand why, say, a military leader who makes a horrendous blunder that costs the lives of countless soldiers and civilians might choose to take his own life. But suicides are more often the result of ordinary, garden-variety false pride. Consider the alpha male who boasts, "I'm not the kind of man women leave! If anyone's going to leave, it's going to be me! Where's my shotgun?" Here is a man for whom rejection at the hands of a woman delivers such a blow to masculine pride as to render continued existence impossible.

Injuries to pride and the threat of being shamed can thus play a large part in triggering an act of suicide. The greater our pride, the more vulnerable we are to insult. The utterly unacceptable circumstance might be falling seriously ill or suffering a disabling or disfiguring injury, being diagnosed with a psychiatric disorder, being rejected by a lover, being fired, losing a ton of money on the stock market, flunking out of college, or even being sent home from school. When a proud person is already depressed and susceptible to thoughts of suicide, events such as these can prove to be the last straw.

I once worked with a retired army major whose wife wanted to leave him. When things didn't go his way in quarrels with his spouse, he had taken to sticking a .45 automatic in his mouth—an approach he'd learned in Vietnam while interrogating prisoners. A .45 in anybody's mouth demands your attention. Pride was our problem: He was not the kind of man women leave. After several weeks of white-knuckle therapy with this arrogant, stern, prideful man, I remarked that, if his wife wanted to leave him, it seemed sort of silly to me that he should have to go down with the sinking ship. The major quickly corrected me: "Sailors go down with their ships, young man, not soldiers!" In an effort to defend myself, I reminded him that I had been a corporal in the same U.S. Army in which he had served. He snarled, "Ha! Just as I expected. Enlisted swine!"

Then he started to laugh. Here was the big-shot major in therapy to save his extremely important life, and his therapist was a mere enlisted-swine psychologist. The more he thought about it, the more he laughed. He laughed until tears came to his eyes. This was progress. He had discovered the capacity to see himself as absurd, and he had been separated a few paces from his pain.

On more than one occasion, I have also been called in to intervene on and attempt to treat men of high reputation caught in situations where, in the opinion of others, they were absolutely and without hesitation going to kill themselves. I count among them several policemen, two military officers, a handful of lawyers, doctors, businessmen, and college professors, and one member of the clergy who had slipped, however temporarily, from his pulpit and stumbled into sin. In itself, this might not have been so bad, but his arrest for public lewdness had made it into the local newspaper. In his eyes, all his exits were blocked, except for the one to heaven, which was always open.

There is, unfortunately, no one more dangerous to his own health and welfare than a proud, upstanding, high-profile man caught suddenly in the bright light of public exposure for a shameful, illegal, or morally corrupt act. If a pistol is within reach as the net closes around him, and no escape is offered, his life may soon be forfeit. Working with such a person is a tricky business, and there is no simple formula for doing it. Of all the suicides that might be prevented, this one is perhaps the most difficult to head off.

An inflated self-image, the fear of looking bad, the refusal to accept imperfection, a tendency to take offense at the slightest of provocations, an inability to tolerate rejection—such issues must be confronted in counseling. But this will require an extra measure of care and sensitivity. Above all, it is critical that such patients be left with some of their pride intact, enough to enable them to save face. You will need to build a therapeutic relationship in which the patient feels respected, and even then the work of therapy will require a delicate touch. The goal is not to puncture the balloon but to gradually let some air out of it— enough so that the patient's self-image no longer seems worth dying to preserve.

27. Self-disclosure

When I mentioned to my patient the retired army major that I had been in the army, I was engaging in self-disclosure. The question of whether therapists should ever divulge information about themselves to patients is controversial. Some say you should never do so; others say you should never not do so. The answer is probably somewhere in between.

If you are working with suicidal people, it is especially likely that at some point the issue of self-disclosure will come up. Suicidal people will often ask, "Have you ever thought about killing yourself?" How you choose to respond to this question is ultimately your call, but here are some guidelines to consider:

- If a patient asks more or less immediately whether you've ever thought of taking your own life, tell the truth. To my knowledge, lying, whether on the part of the therapist or the patient, has never helped to further a therapeutic relationship. If you instead fall back on the old therapist stall, "I don't think that's an appropriate question," you run the risk of making someone who is already feeling bad feel even worse for having said something inappropriate. You may also have hindered the development of trust.

- If the answer to your patient's question is yes— that is, if at some point in your life you did give serious thought to suicide and perhaps made one or more attempts—sharing a few of the details may be helpful. But aim to keep your account relatively brief. The goal is provide enough information to let your patient know you've "been there," not to turn the therapy hour into *your* therapy hour.

- Such a disclosure may prove especially valuable if you received some of the same kind of help you're now giving to others. The message, "See, therapy works!" is very powerful. It gives a patient hope.

Greater candor reinforces a sense of connection between two human beings and fosters mutual trust. The downside to self-disclosure is that you risk undermining your placebo effect. The more a patient knows about you, the more human you become, which tends to tarnish your halo. Upon learning you too were once suicidal, your patient may be tempted to see you as emotionally frail or unstable or to wonder, "Jeez! Isn't anyone sane anymore?" So before letting a patient in on some aspect of your life, always pause and think about the effect the information is likely to have. In the case of your own experience with suicidal thoughts, keep the emphasis on recovery—on the fact that, even though you've had some hard times, you made it through them and went on to enjoy life again.

28. Imagining the Worst

This technique consists of a series of questions that prompt a patient to set aside the notion of suicide for a moment and consider the worst possible consequences of the present crisis. The idea here is to extricate a suicidal person from the intolerable present, the one filled with what he or she perceives to be unbearable psychological pain. Obliging patients to imagine the worst that could happen if they absolutely had to continue living carries them past the present endpoint of suicide and helps to get at the very fears that may very well be driving the desire to die.

> *Patient:* He's leaving and I can't stand it.
> *Therapist:* What's the worst that could happen if he left?
> *Patient:* He can't leave!
> *Therapist:* I understand how you feel, but what's the worst that could happen if he did leave?
> *Patient:* I'd . . . I'd be lost.
> *Therapist:* Then what's the worst that could happen?
> *Patient:* I . . . I . . . I don't think I can live without him.
> *Therapist:* But if he left, and you had to live without him, what's the worst that could happen?
> *Patient:* I'd be alone.

Therapist: Yes, you'd be alone. And you'd probably feel a little lost, like you did before you met him.

Patient: But I hate being alone. I mean, I really, like, *hate* it!

Therapist: But suppose you had to be alone. What's the worst that could happen?

Patient: Well, if I had to be alone . . . well, I guess I'd have to be. For a while anyway.

The future is where fear lies, and patients sometimes need a gentle shove into the reality of that future. The suicidal mind may have been tiptoeing up to the edge of some vast, terrifying forever, taking a quick look, and then backing quickly away. But each time the person backs away their present fears are unconsciously reinforced.

Like a kid watching a horror movie, suicidal people keep their faces covered with their hands and peek through their fingers. In such cases, our job is to get their hands down from their faces and ask them to have a square look at whatever it is they fear—that "something" lurking just around the corner. By gently asking, again and again, what the very worst would bring, you give form and substance to their fear—and a known fear is always more manageable than a vague one. In this way, moving them beyond present miseries and forward into the future can help to revive hope.

If you meet resistance to this line of questioning, you can simply say, "Look, we know suicide will get you out of this situation and put you far beyond any fear. And, for a fact, you won't ever have to solve another problem, feel any more pain, or face any more uncertainties. But suppose you had no choice but to stay alive. What's the worst that could happen then?"

29. Plan B

I use Plan B all the time, with all sorts of patients, not just suicidal ones. The Plan B approach begins with Plan A.

Whatever the patient has been doing—his or her life to date, including goals and expectations—is Plan A. And the point is that Plan A hasn't been working very well.

In the case of a suicidal patient, once I have a good sense of the person's history and can sum up what has been going on that has culminated in the forever decision, I play back the patient's own description of the fix that he or she is in. Then I agree that the situation is both intolerable and hopeless. This amounts to supporting the negative side of the patient's ambivalence about life and his or her typically constricted view of the present problem.

I have uniformly found it countertherapeutic to disagree with patients about how sick or suicidal *they* think they are. When it comes to the patient's own private experience of pain, my opinion couldn't matter less. I have seen more than one patient attempt suicide after being told by a professional, "I understand that you're very distressed, but I wouldn't say that you're seriously suicidal." So I have the utmost respect for the sufferer's view of how serious things are.

Basically, then, I concur with all the patient's reasons for being suicidal. This affirmation of the hopelessness of the situation almost invariably produces a relieved sigh and a comment such as, "Thank God, someone *finally* understands." Once the patient lets me know that my summation dovetails reasonably well with the patient's own assessment of the problem ("Yeah, that's how it is all right"), then I say, "Okay. That's Plan A. What's Plan B?"

"Plan B?"

"Yes. Now don't tell me you've spent all these years working on Plan A without a backup plan? You know, a Plan B—what you were going to do if Plan A didn't work out."

"Huh?"

Far too many people in this world do not have a Plan B. We just muddle through life with Plan A. Plan A can be that job you've been angling for at the factory, or taking over the family business, or becoming a doctor, or marrying your high school sweetheart. Plan A is what you've always wanted—the way you think life should be. When Plan A is working out, you feel happy and rewarded, and life is fun living. Plan A is great.

Unfortunately, bad stuff happens. Call it chance, fate, or providence: The cause matters a lot less than the consequences. All it takes for Plan A to go up in smoke is for the factory to close, the family business to be forced into bankruptcy, the practice of medicine to become impossibly stressful, or your high school sweetheart to leave you for someone else. With Plan A in ashes, what's a person to do?

What you do is grieve, take a deep breath, and maybe kneel down and utter a prayer or two. Then you take Plan B down off the shelf and start a new life. Most of the suicidal people I've met do not have a Plan B, however, let alone a Plan C or D.

Plan B can be *anything*. To get patients unfrozen from their decision to die while standing neck deep in Plan A, I tell them that they do not actually have to live out Plan B. But they at least owe it to themselves to imagine what Plan B might be like. It doesn't have to be realistic, although as you and the patient work on creating it, Plan B often begins to look more and more viable. In fact, Plan B can turn out to be a whole lot more rewarding and more fun than Plan A ever was.

Yes, some folks will resist. "That's impossible," they'll say. "There's no way I could ever . . ." This is followed by any of 1,001 reasonable-sounding excuses for not changing one's life. To which I say, "I understand that, and you can always keep plugging away at Plan A. But what's the harm in dreaming?"

Spinning "impossible" scenarios for the future is something only human beings can do, and persuading suicidal people to do it can free them up in amazing ways. Like those spirited prisoners who are forced to live as inmates (Plan A) but who keep hope alive by actively scheming, dreaming, and working on a means to escape (Plan B), so too can suicidal people find hope by imagining a life other than the one they are prepared to die to be rid of. The effect here can be quite dramatic.

I have found the Plan B exercise to be especially powerful when I ask patients not merely to think about what another life might look like but to actually write out a description. I ask them for details—where they would live, what kind of house or apartment they would want to have, whether they would need additional schooling and where would they get it, what sort of hobbies they might take up, and so on. The more details the better: The clearer your view of the territory ahead, the easier it is to venture into it.

Because working up a Plan B requires energy and imagination, it may be more than a seriously depressed patient can handle. But once the person has had some treatment and begins to feel better, the Plan B approach can be very helpful. My experience has been that, once people have any sort of backup plan at all, the tension and the sense of impending doom that they were experiencing begin to evaporate very quickly.

30. Resurrecting Dreams

This approach goes hand in hand with helping folks develop a Plan B. It begins from the notion that all of us, when we were young, had dreams. We might have dreamed of becoming a forest ranger, a rocket scientist, a lawyer, a painter, a stand-up comic, or a songwriter. It doesn't matter what the dream was—only that we once dreamed it.

They say that without our dreams, we die. Certainly, once you kill yourself, you forsake all your dreams—including the ones you never even attempted to turn into realities. By an act of self-destruction, you say, in effect, I give

up all my dreams. But wait a minute. Before you kill yourself, could you tell us what those dreams were?

When you were a child, what did you most want to be when you grew up?
What wild and crazy thing have you always wanted to do that you won't
ever have the chance to do once you're dead?
What promises did you make to yourself? What did you tell yourself that
someday you would do, when you finally had the time and/or the
guts to give it a try?
If you kill yourself, who will cherish those dreams?

This questioning often leads to grief for noble deeds
never done, mountains never climbed, rivers never
crossed, words never spoken, and songs never sung. But
that's okay. Allowing ourselves to feel the sorrow of what
could have been frees us to reach out for the joy of what still
might be.

And so I try to prompt suicidal people to talk about the
dreams they will leave on the shelf. I usually begin by asking
something like, "Remember back when you were a kid? The
way you dreamed about growing up? Do you remember
what you wanted to be, or something you always wanted to
do? Can you tell me what it was?"

This should be a gentle, but persistent, challenge. I
often use the image of a dream stored away high on a shelf
where nobody can find it but the dreamer. The dream,
written on a slip of paper and rolled up and tied with a red
ribbon, has been secreted away because others somehow
convinced the dreamer that it was foolish, or immature, or
impractical. Or perhaps the dreamer was led to believe that
he or she had no right to dream dreams, no right to aspire
to something different. But is this a valid conclusion? I
encourage the patient to take the dream down from the
shelf and have another look at it to see whether, just maybe,
he or she ought to go ahead and try to breathe life into it.

If I encounter resistance—"It's too late for me," "I'm too old to start over"—I remind the patient that Colonel Sanders didn't start frying his own chicken until he got his first Social Security check. I remind them that ten years from now we're going to be ten years older, no matter what. So why not dust off one of those old dreams and give it a go?

But if they are ever to come true, our dreams must be concrete, clear, vivid, and specific. The dream needs to be laid out and written down, and the details filled in. Once this happens, the dream has become a Plan B. It has been given wheels and, powered by hope, it can roll forward into the future.

31. Being Someone's Teddy Bear

To the question, "So, how's it going?" June Carter Cash used to answer, "Still trying to matter." When we feel that we matter, that we are of value to others, the risk of suicide is reduced. But suicidal people often feel that no one needs them.

To be needed by others is to be somebody's teddy bear—the person who provides unconditional love and comfort to someone else. The teddy bear idea came to me from a favorite Shanahan *New Yorker* cartoon in which two police officers are trying to talk a suicidal teddy bear in from the ledge of a high-rise building. One of the officers is saying, "There's an Officer Ripley in here who could use a hug." And we know, instantly, that now the teddy bear cannot jump. Once he has been reminded that others need his love, his suicide becomes impossible.

The need to be needed should never be underestimated. Feeling that, far from being needed, one is in fact a burden on others may lead to the feeling that one is intolerably alone, and such unbearable psychological pain can lead, in turn, to the desire to be dead (Rudd et al. 2006; Williams, Duggan, Crane, and Fennell 2006; Shneidman 1998;

Baumeister and Leary 1995). In his excellent book *Why People Die by Suicide* (Joiner 2005), Thomas Joiner persuasively argues that a thwarted need to belong and the feeling that one is a burden on others are two of the three necessary but insufficient conditions for suicide. Research suggests that women who are responsible for the welfare of others, particularly if the others are children, are at a lower risk for suicide. In fact, mothers and pregnant women are among those least likely to die by their own hand (Marzuk et al. 1997). You can't, if you're a reasonably thoughtful and caring person, just go off and kill yourself and leave those who are dependent on you to fend for themselves.

Therapy must address the suicidal person's feeling that, if he or she were to die, no one would really notice or care. Gently but stubbornly, the patient's belief that he or she is not needed must be challenged. In addition, if suicidal people can be persuaded to do something that requires getting out of themselves and into the life of someone else, so much the better. An act of charity or a gesture of goodwill toward others makes us feel that our lives have meaning. I have recommended to suicidal patients that they volunteer in a nursing home or send a card to someone who is ill or buy a homeless person something to eat. I have tried to show them that giving of themselves to others will make them feel good.

I remember working with a particularly angry woman who hated humankind but loved animals. After I wondered aloud whether the animals in the local shelter might need her attention, she volunteered her time for a while. Later on, she was hired by a veterinarian to work in his small animal clinic.

Sad to say, though, suicidal people are often so preoccupied with their own suffering, and their ability to reason clearly so impaired, that they find it difficult to imagine what they might mean to others. But the fact remains that their love and support are much in demand. Everywhere people are hug deprived—children, parents, friends, relatives, the elderly and neglected, the homeless. Even stray cats could stand to be petted (and I'm not fond of cats).

We all need to be someone's teddy bear. Once I have established a trusting relationship with suicidal patients, especially those who believe they don't matter to anyone, I often try to unwrap the arms they've been using to hug their own pain and get them wrapped around someone else. Because creatures who are hugged hug back.

32. Pets

A woman at a workshop once asked me whether caring for a pet might be a protective factor against suicide. I said I was sure it was, but I was curious why she had asked. She then told me the story of her mother's death. Her mother, who was in her mid-seventies and had been widowed for three years, was desperately depressed but was receiving no treatment. Her sole companion was her cat. Following repeated entreaties that she leave the Midwest of her childhood and move out to California to live with her son and his family, she finally agreed.

"Good!" said her son. "Now, you know we want you to come, but we can't have the cat. Alice has allergies. So you'll have to leave the cat behind."

After a pause on the line, the mother said, "I understand. Well, I have a couple of things I need to do now." And she hung up.

Within two days of making this statement she took her much-loved cat to the veterinarian and had it put to sleep. On the drive back to her home she died in a high-speed crash into a utility pole. It was estimated that she was going over 90 miles per hour at the time. She did not have to move to California. Her death was officially called an accident, and the cause was never questioned. But how this accident could have happened remained a family puzzle.

Was this suicide? We will never know. But what we do know is that being responsible for other living things helps keep people alive. So does loving someone else, including a pet. Especially for those who otherwise live alone, the love of and for a pet can be an important protective factor— and, not surprisingly, there is a growing literature that supports pet therapy. If you think that a suicidal person might profit by having a pet and that he or she could be entrusted with an animal's care, it is a possibility well worth suggesting.

33. Putting Problems in Perspective

Suicidal people are typically overwhelmed by what seems to them the sheer enormity of their problems. Whatever the situation facing them, it feels vast and insurmountable. From the outside looking in, we may not think that their problems, however real they may be, are worth dying over. But, as we know, our view of their suffering matters little in comparison to their own. The trick is, then, to persuade suicidal people to step back from their own misery for a moment so that they can gain some perspective.

Insensitive, knee-jerk comparisons—"You think *you've* got it bad? What about those poor kids living on the streets!"—only make the crisis worse, especially if they are delivered early on in counseling. But once the suicidal person has passed through the initial crisis, has had the benefit of some treatment, and has decided, at least for now, to live, the following strategy can prove helpful.

Ask the person to imagine putting all of his or her problems onto a great big table with all the other problems faced by all the other people around the world.

It takes a big table because the human race has a lot of problems.

Now tell the person that he or she can trade his or her own big problems for any other set of big problems that someone else on the planet is facing.

Let your patient think it over for a while.

What you will often find is that after considering the problems with which other people must contend, most of us—including suicidal people—would just as soon stick with our own problems. This shift in perspective often allows the suicidal sufferer to understand, in concrete terms, that his or her woes are probably not so enormous or so unique that they cannot somehow be mastered. After all, if other people have found ways to cope with their miseries, then perhaps we can do the same.

Taking a fresh perspective can help even seriously depressed patients begin to believe that their problems are manageable. It fosters hope, which in turn renews their commitment to therapy. The growing awareness that even big problems have solutions gives a suicidal person a powerful reason to continue learning how to find those solutions. Given a little faith that a path through suffering does exist, the person may eventually come to agree that our problems are rarely worth dying over.

34. Good People in Impossible Situations

As we have seen, people sometimes become suicidal because they find themselves in what seems to them an impossible situation. Sometimes these perceptions are distorted, but sometimes they are right. For almost any given personality, there are bound to be truly impossible situations, impossible relationships, impossible jobs, or impossible living conditions—circumstances that make life unlivable. In a word, someone can be a good person in a bad place. Except in prison camps and jails, however, people who are otherwise sane and sober seldom resort to suicide simply because they are caught in a bad situation. Rather, suicide comes to seem a desirable solution only after the person has developed psychiatric symptoms, usually of severe anxiety and/or clinical depression.

Over the years I have seen far too many basically sound, healthy people who were trapped in circumstances that were fundamentally at odds with their values. Among them was a compassionate and highly principled nurse who had the misfortune of working for a nursing home that was more interested in its bottom line than in the quality of care it provided its patients. As a cost-cutting measure, it had reduced its staff, with the result that this good nurse was confronted daily with situations that compromised patient care. The necessity of working under such conditions violated her core beliefs and her sense of right and wrong. She could not sleep, she was losing weight, and she became depressed.

Another patient was an attorney and a devout Catholic who held himself to high moral standards. For ten years he had worked in a firm surrounded by colleagues whose ethics were questionable and for whom he had no respect. He was caught in a cesspool of corruption and could not see a way out. His way of adapting to what was for him a living hell was to become so depressed that he was unable to get out of bed and make it into the office.

Helping someone caught in a bad life situation requires first that you gain a thorough understanding of the person you are working with and a clear sense of how their personal values are being thwarted or threatened. The question that will need answering is, Does this person fit into the life he or she is living? If you look for the frustrated psychological needs first, the stress points will show themselves quickly.

Sometimes the problem lies with a lack of fit between a person's talents and temperament and the demands of a specific job. Someone who is creative and free-spirited is not going to have much fun turning nuts on bolts for

General Motors, any more than someone who is meticulous and highly controlled is likely to enjoy working with a roomful of kindergarteners. In such cases, simply suggesting, "Maybe you just weren't cut out to be a salesman" (or a lawyer, nurse, electrician, farmer, theatrical agent, therapist, or whatever) can provide relief. Given that careers are more likely to be decided by random opportunity than by deliberate reflection and career counseling, severely depressed people often find it very enlightening to explore how they ended up doing what they are doing. It is also worth reminding folks that over a full life span most of us will have at least three distinct careers. Realizing that other people do make changes can give sufferers a sense of freedom and the flexibility they need to reconsider their choices and move on.

Very often the problem lies specifically with clashes between a person's fundamental beliefs and values and those of other people or of the organization in which the person works. Many suicidal people have been struggling for years in situations and relationships that are deeply antithetical to their needs, their personalities, and their dreams and, as a result, have become seriously depressed. They feel hopeless, and they despair of change. The possibility that they are actually perfectly okay, even nice, people caught up in unhappy circumstances may not even have occurred to them. I once counseled a suicidal insurance salesman who hated himself for having to high-pressure old people into buying policies they didn't need. "What's a decent fellow like you doing in a job like this?" I asked. "I don't know," he replied, as if he'd never thought about it before. "What *am* I doing?"

Affirming that the patient is a worthy soul who is simply trapped in a bad situation gives the person permission to start thinking about a way out. Hitherto unimagined exits suddenly open up. Moreover, because some of the blame for the patient's present suffering can now be shifted to external conditions, the patient is able to regain some sense of self-esteem.

I remember working with a senior corporate executive had been brought in by his wife because he was talking about suicide. His former boss—a benevolent man who had founded the company for which this man worked—had died, and now his four sons were running the company. The sons were not benevolent people. While my patient was overseas on a business trip, they had used the occasion of his absence to strip him of his job title, his influence, and his stock options, actions that all but forced him to resign.

His wife and friends were surprised when he refused to file an age discrimination suit against the company's new chief executives or otherwise fight back. So I asked him why he wasn't more interested in ripping their heads off. "When I was a boy," he replied, "I always wanted to be a man of God—a priest, actually. I'm gentle and forgiving at heart. Revenge just isn't in me." So then I asked him what a nice guy like him was doing keeping company with a bunch of young cutthroats in the first place. He admitted that, until he returned from his trip, he hadn't recognized just how malicious and greedy they were. But now that he did, he said, it was probably a good thing he was no longer with the company. The more he thought about it, the more he realized he would never want that job back. In the end, he concluded that perhaps they had done him a favor.

Some time later, I ran into this man at our local airport. He had taken a new job, which happened to be with one of his former firm's competitors. This new firm was now doing very well, and it was eating deeply into his old company's share of the market—a sweet revenge, if ever there was one.

I have also counseled people trapped in relationships so unloving and so filled with anger and mistrust that each new day was a dreaded event. Toxic relationships, because they are stressful, can make people sick in mind and body. When a relationship grows to be so stressful and so soul crushing that it triggers major depression and thoughts of suicide, it needs to be either fixed or ended. We are lucky that the laws governing marriage no longer oblige us to remain in a relationship that is endangering our health and destroying our spirit.

For a patient struggling with a relationship that has become impossible, a simple suggestion such as, "Maybe you and Shirley weren't made for each other after all," can again be remarkably freeing. It shifts the patient away from the notion of blame—from the idea that either the patient or his or her partner must be the one at fault in this mess— and from the sense of personal failure that so often accompanies a dying relationship. It also opens up the possibility that out there, somewhere, another, more suitable mate awaits.

People who have wound up in the wrong place often feel locked into the choices they once made and may be kicking themselves for having made the choices they did. I have thus found it very helpful to relieve patients of the weight of their own past decisions by saying, "You know, we all make the best choices we can. We use the best information we have at the time, and then we just do it. There's no other way. But sometimes we don't have enough reliable information, especially about ourselves, and maybe that's what happened here. What do you think?"

Once sufferers come to understand that, like the rest of us who have to make choices, they will never have the perfect information and the perfect insights that would allow them to arrive at perfect decisions, they can stop feeling so guilty and beating themselves up for being so stupid. Making what later turn out to be mistakes is an inescapable fact of life. It's why they put erasers on pencils.

35. Deep Breathing

Many suicidal people are laboring under both acute and chronic stress. As a result, not only their minds but also their bodies feel out of control. To help them gain some degree of mastery over feelings of discomfort and panic, I often teach them a simple breathing technique, one that amounts, quite literally, to a sigh of relief.

I begin by explaining that deep breathing generally produces relaxation. Then I instruct the patient as follows:

- "Inhale deeply and hold your breath for a count of four seconds: one-thousand-one, one-thousand-two, one-thousand-three, one-thousand-four." I usually count along with the patient the first few times.
- At the end of the count, I tell the patient, "Now exhale through your mouth while we count to four again. You will feel the tension flow out with the air."
- I have the patient repeat the pattern for several minutes. Most people report feeling a sense of calm, and even physical relaxation, almost immediately.
- I then help the patient identify this internal state as one of calm and control. I often call it "getting centered."
- I instruct the patient to practice this deep breathing twice a day, or, if it seems helpful, more often.

As I explain to patients, whenever they find themselves caught in a stressful situation or having thoughts of suicide, they can practice some deep breathing. If they remember to do this each time they start to feel anxious and overwhelmed or thinking about suicide, it should help them to recover a sense of balance. While inhaling and exhaling, they can say to themselves, "This too will pass."

Not only does this relaxation technique give patients some on-the-spot control over what feels to them out of control, but it can also teach them to recognize the conditions that tend to provoke self-destructive thoughts—the events, the kinds of interactions, and the overall circumstances that often generate such thoughts. I often ask a patient to take a moment after the crisis has passed to jot down what was happening (thoughts, feelings, outside events) just before they felt the need to do some deep breathing to relax. The goal here is to capture the chain of events that triggered their sense of anxiety and distress. Just as people write down their dreams so that they can remember them and analyze them, recording one's experience at a particular moment may lead to the discovery of specific negative thoughts or feelings that appear to be associated with the impulse to suicide. Such information is clearly very valuable when we are seeking to understand what is driving suicidal behavior.

Severely stressed or anxiety-ridden patients may profit from more formal relaxation training, such as biofeedback. But deep breathing is remarkably effective. It is also a wonderfully portable relaxation method, one that can be practiced any time, any place.

36. Suicide Dreamers

"The thought of suicide is a powerful solace," Friedrich Nietzsche once remarked; "by means of it one gets through many a bad night." But some people carry a good thing too far. I have in mind my work with several patients for whom thoughts of death had become a central theme of life itself. Over the course of their therapy, they taught me how thinking about suicide can grow to be a comforting and familiar habit.

"Suicide dreamers" describe themselves as plagued by frequent and repetitive suicidal thoughts, and yet these thoughts are not typically associated with high-risk or overtly suicidal behavior. In other words, although these patients think about suicide frequently, even obsessively, they rarely get beyond the thinking phase. These low-grade suicidal ideations do not merely occur in the days and weeks following the onset of an episode of acute depression but may in fact persist for months, years, and even decades. While such thoughts do not, at least in my observation, directly culminate in actual suicide attempts, they just as surely lay the foundation upon which an attempt could later be based.

It appears that this "suicide dreaming" is a kind of default mental activity or psychological reflex, often triggered by some unpleasant or stressful event. Odd though it might seem, these persistent suicidal ruminations serve to reduce anxiety for the sufferer, just as Nietzsche observed. Entering this fantasy realm of suicide produces a sense of calm and relaxation. As a form of mental escape, it is probably a conditioned response, one that lowers the autonomic nervous system's overall level of arousal and may even have addictive qualities. In this self-induced hypnotic state, thinking of suicide functions as a kind of psychic tranquilizer that, taken in small doses in times of stress, conflict, or loss, can provide on-demand relief from the pain of existence. Patients thus self-trained are often very invested in their preferred method of escape from psychological suffering and will not be easily persuaded to give it up.

In the cases I have treated, dreaming of suicide had become a well-established cognitive habit, a routine mode of imagining death, characterized by deeply entrenched thoughts and repetitive melancholy themes. Sometimes patients had chosen a special setting, which served as a stimulus to their fantasies, and some had selected music to enhance the mood. Several had even developed elaborate funeral scenes, complete with music, flowers, and pallbearers. In one case, the faces of the survivors were clearly visible to the suicidal person as the casket was lowered away.

Strongly ingrained habits of thinking are stubbornly resistant to change and thus difficult to extinguish. Because suicide dreamers are typically anxious about their behavior, I often begin by reassuring such patients that just because a person thinks a lot about suicide does not mean he or she has to act on those thoughts. I remind them that we human beings are free to imagine any damn thing we want to—it's what we do that counts. This drives a wedge between thought and action, which reduces tension. I also point out that people who passively dream about suicide are not usually the impulsive sort. And so it is not very likely that as they are contentedly fantasizing about suicide, they will suddenly jump up and kill themselves.

Beyond that, treatment for suicide dreamers can include any of the standard approaches to psychotherapy and, if appropriate, medication. In particular, I try to teach such patients something about the underlying purpose of their repetitive cognitions and how they most likely came by them. I explain that humans learn through reinforcement, stimulus-response, and social conditioning, along with a bit of help from our neurochemistry. I also explain how we develop habits, including unpleasant cognitive ones. But if bad habits are learned, they can also be unlearned.

This is fundamental stuff, and I try to keep it simple and nonjudgmental. I stress that we learn to repeat, again and again, whatever makes us feel good or reduces anxiety. If we discover that lying down to listen to sad music and dream about suicide reduces tension and provides an escape from a world of distress, then this will likely become a habit. By acknowledging the powerful tonic their suicide dreaming provides them, I help such patients accept their obsessive thoughts as a way of coping, one often used by troubled persons who have been unable to come up with other solutions to the problems facing them. This approach normalizes the process whereby such patients came by their familiar habits of thought.

Once patients have learned to identify cognitive cues to relaxation—the feelings and thoughts that make us anxious and prompt us to seek relief—I begin to offer alternative responses to these cues. The idea is to shift chronically suicidal patients away from the escapist solution offered by fantasies of self-destruction and encourage more proactive, problem-solving approaches to distress. This process involves explanation, psycho-education, gentle confrontation, paradoxical instruction, practice sessions in cognitive retraining, and redefining problems in ways that suggest new solutions.

Because suicide dreamers are often passive people with weak self-esteem, some form of assertiveness training can also be helpful. So can group therapy, especially for patients who tend to be isolated and are struggling to get their needs met within their limited social network. In addition, I have at times found it valuable to ask patients to express their dark thoughts on paper, by keeping a journal or writing poetry, or in drawings or music. Such expressive activities are useful because they transform subjective experience into something external to the self and thus separate the sufferer from his or her thoughts. But creative self-expression is also very freeing, and it often promotes greater self-understanding.

37. Paradoxical Suggestions

This is an intervention that can prove very helpful with patients who are obsessed with thoughts of suicide, such as the suicide dreamers just described. It is an approach that should be used with some caution, however, and, like many of the interventions described in this chapter, only after you've established a firm therapeutic alliance with your patient. For reasons that will be obvious, this is not a sensible strategy to pursue if a patient has ever acted upon suicidal thoughts or seems at all likely to do so. You will also need to be sure that a patient is not suffering from obsessive-compulsive disorder. If the patient's recurrent thoughts of suicide do meet the diagnostic criteria for this disorder, medication may be in order.

Simply put, a paradoxical suggestion asks the patient to do even more of what he or she is already doing. The paradox here is that magnifying a symptom can actually serve to reduce it by increasing the patient's control over it. To someone who is plagued with repetitive and intrusive suicidal thoughts, I might start by saying, "Just so I can get some idea about how much time you actually spend thinking about suicide, I'd like you to take this index card and keep track of the total minutes, or hours, you spend doing so this week. You can think about suicide as much as you like." This request immediately places the patient in the role of both collaborator and scientific observer, requiring him or her to isolate and measure what has been perceived as seamless and pervasive. If the patient reports spending an average of forty minutes each day thinking about suicide, I might then suggest, "Hmm . . . I wonder . . . As an experiment for the coming week, I'd like you to think about suicide for at least an hour each day. Nothing else for now—just suicide. And keep track of your time."

Understandably, therapists are sometimes frightened by obsessive thoughts of suicide and so are tempted to tell a patient, "Stop that—you're scaring me!" Others may worry that encouraging a patient to think about suicide might just prompt an attempt. But requiring patients to pay close attention to a symptom and even to deliberately exaggerate it actually shifts control to the patient. I often combine this intervention with bibliotherapy, by asking the patient to read one of the many excellent popular books about suicide, which again obliges the person to think consciously about the subject.

As I have said, comforting habits of thought that provide relief from emotional distress can be difficult to dislodge. In and of itself, the technique of paradoxical suggestion is unlikely to produce a cure. You will still need to work on fostering self-awareness and on helping suicide dreamers learn to substitute good habits for bad and otherwise find new solutions to old problems.

38. Working with Chronically Suicidal People

Karl Menninger used the term *chronic suicide* to refer to cases in which someone who finds the idea of suicide unacceptable, possibly even repugnant, nevertheless chooses to die a slow death by abusing drugs or alcohol or engaging in other life-threatening behavior (Menninger 1938). I use the term somewhat differently. My chronically suicidal patients are those for whom being suicidal has essentially become a way of life. They have often made multiple attempts at suicide, obviously none of them successful, often because the methods employed were not very likely to be lethal.

I once received a letter from a woman who boasted that she had made over three thousand attempts on her life. She said she was willing to wager that I had "never met anyone so suicidal." Given that I've met quite a few people who subsequently killed themselves, often on the very first attempt, her comment made me wonder whether her definition of *suicidal* was perhaps somewhat different from my own.

Indeed, the clinician may well be prompted to ask whether the behavior of the chronically suicidal might not better be described as attention-seeking. The answer to this question is probably yes—but that does not mean such behavior should be dismissed as merely manipulative or that it might not someday lead to death.

Although I am not an expert in the diagnosis and treatment of chronically suicidal patients, I know many who are, and over the years I have worked with several such patients myself. As they have shown me, being suicidal can confer certain rights and obligations, just like any other social role or public identity. People who constantly threaten suicide or engage in suicidal behavior in an effort to control those around them eventually become known for their distinctive form of interpersonal communication.

Very often, those who become chronically suicidal grew up in seriously dysfunctional families in which their basic needs—including the need to have their emotions, especially negative ones such as anger or fear, acknowledged and validated—were constantly thwarted. And so they learned to resort to more extreme measures. As they discovered, the five simple words "I want to kill myself" can be counted on to produce an immediate reaction. For instance:

- Those around you stop whatever they are doing and pay attention to you.
- Those who have been mistreating you stop mistreating you—at least for a while.
- People who are threatening to leave you stop threatening to leave you. (After all, how could they abandon a dying person?)
- People who are about to fire you, give you an F, expel you from school, keep you in jail, or otherwise take punitive action against you may reconsider their plans.
- Doctors, clergymen, therapists, counselors, and others who give aid and assistance to people in pain can be persuaded to give even more aid and assistance.

Our common humanity insists that we seek to prevent

death, including death by suicide. Just as we believe it is better to let one hundred guilty people go free than to execute an innocent person, we would prefer to overreact to one hundred suicidal people who will never actually kill themselves than to ignore the single one who will. If someone appears to be suicidal, we will therefore do everything humanly possible to keep that person from dying. As, of course, we should.

For the chronically suicidal, this means that a safe harbor can usually be found, provided the rescue signal they send is loud and clear and is accepted by the people on the receiving end. The chronically suicidal have had considerable experience with how people respond to suicidal threats and gestures, and they have learned very well how to make their wishes known and how to force calm from an emotional storm. They know the drill.

Working with someone who has learned to cope with all of life's struggles by playing the trump card of suicidal threats is no easy matter. Treatment is especially challenging because chronically suicidal people are so often diagnosed with borderline personality disorder. The etiology of this disorder is complex, but it may be that some individuals are born with a hypersensitivity to sources of agitation and stress. Individuals diagnosed with BPD typically have a very weak sense of self-identity and are haunted by feelings of emptiness and low self-worth. In a desperate effort to avoid abandonment and to get their needs met, they tend to shift back and forth between a passive, approval-seeking stance and violent displays of emotion and other attention-getting behavior, including various forms of self-harm. Their relationships with others are typically intense and highly turbulent. As patients, they can make enormous emotional demands on a therapist and may also be difficult to keep in treatment. Because a significant number of such patients eventually die by suicide, doing therapy with the chronically suicidal is much riskier than working with someone whose diagnostic profile is less complicated.

Through their behavior over the years, perennially suicidal individuals have typically created negative expectations in others—expectations that they will, in fact, kill themselves. Now they are trapped. Part of our task, then, is to protect them from feeling obliged to live down to these expectations of an early death by suicide. At the same time, because chronically suicidal people can so easily seem manipulative, they can generate negative feelings in you, the healer. Your anger and impatience, whether openly expressed or hidden behind a forced smile, can prove very destructive, even lethal, for the suicidal person. As a son once said to his father, who had been talking about suicide for months in the wake of a divorce, "Dad, I'm real tired of listening to this. If you're going to kill yourself, why don't you just go ahead and get it over with?" Unbeknownst to the son, his father was holding a pistol to his head while they were talking. Following his exasperated challenge, the son heard not only the shot but also his father's body hitting the floor.

As therapists, we must help these challenging patients change the way they behave—how they manage emotions and how they interact with others. Fortunately, thanks to the pioneering work of University of Washington psychologist Marsha Linehan, we now have evidence-based and effective interventions for use with the chronically suicidal. In the early 1990s, Linehan developed a treatment method now known as dialectical behavior therapy. Founded on the cognitive-behavioral approach, DBT is a highly structured set of techniques in which the therapist works closely with the patient to address specific situations that come up in the patient's life. The emphasis is on the reduction of maladaptive behavior—first and foremost suicidal behavior and other forms of self-injury—and on the acquisition of skills that enable patients to find more appropriate solutions to emotionally difficult events. In addition to individual therapy, patients attend skills-training sessions, which are usually conducted in group format (see Linehan et al. 1991; Linehan 1993a and 1993b). Professional training in this intervention is now available around the world. If you work with persistently suicidal persons, I strongly recommend that you complete such a training program.

CONCLUSION
Caring for Ourselves, Caring for Others

THERE IS SOMETHING fundamentally daunting about spending a good portion of our lives trying to talk people out of ending theirs. But that is exactly what some of us have chosen to do. Day after day, we invest not only time and energy in our work but part of ourselves as well. To be effective in what we do, we must guide, assist, and sometimes push troubled patients into experiencing the strong emotions, painful memories, and sources of conflict that have brought them to the brink of self-destruction. Anything less probably won't be enough. So, necessarily, we do much of our work in an emotionally charged atmosphere.

If we wish to be successful in this business of saving lives, as well as remain optimistic about the work we do, we need to have our ideals—but we also need to be realistic, especially about ourselves. And so, to anyone who works with suicidal people, I would offer some basic advice:

- Be aware that, unless you somehow manage to screen out all suicidal individuals before they ever step inside your office, you are going to end up working with suicidal people. Prepare yourself. Read books. Take some training in suicide risk detection, assessment, and management.
- If at all possible, limit the number of actively suicidal patients with whom you are working at any one time. People who have survived their suicide

crisis and are on the mend don't keep you up at night; people who are teetering on the edge are another matter. Try not to overindulge in this exciting work.

- Share every case. Recommendations that could mean the difference between life and death should never be made by someone in isolation. If you are still in training, consultation with supervisors is essential. A formal debriefing after a tough session or a difficult decision helps even seasoned practitioners understand that they have done their best. It also proves a powerful inoculation against stress, especially if a patient dies.

- However we are trained, we should be comfortable with the subject of suicide and its inherent preoccupation with violence and death. Some therapists take a chill when a patient mentions suicide. Others feel a stab of anxiety. This is okay. But if talk of suicide causes you to freeze, panic, or otherwise become undone, then you need to work your way through your anxieties (and, if you are unable to do so, you might want to consider another line of work). A therapist who is too frightened to think clearly enough to solve problems is of little use to a suicidal patient. If you must occasionally panic, then panic later, when the patient isn't around. When I need to panic, I have always found that getting together with colleagues is very helpful.

- Healers must learn to see the human being in the suicidal sufferer, not some strange or perverse creature whose thoughts and behavior are essentially unfathomable. It helps to understand that the person we're trying to help is *just like us* in all the essential ways that make human beings a single species—or, to put it another way, it helps to see ourselves as ordinary, not extraordinary. Remember that our capacity to heal will be limited unless our patients believe us to be warm, understanding, and genuine in our concern. Garden-variety compassion will save more suicidal sufferers than a box full of technical skills.

- That said, we need special knowledge. There is much to learn about suicide and its causes, and the information is available. We need to understand how suicidal people think and where these thoughts tend to come from, and we need to learn what can be done to keep our patients safe while they get better. This does not require a PhD, but it does oblige us to read a book about the subject now and then and review the published research from time to time. To anyone who seeks to understand suicide, I would heartily recommend two terrific books I mentioned earlier: Kay Redfield Jamison's *Night Falls Fast* and Thomas Joiner's *Why People Die by Suicide*. In addition, Jerome Groopman's *The Anatomy of Hope: How People Prevail in the Face of Illness* offers compelling testimony to the healing power of hope.

- We also need a supportive work environment. We need to be respected, even honored, for what we do. Saving lives is serious business. If we are to maintain a positive attitude about ourselves and our jobs, not only must a good professional backup system be available to us, but we need to like the people we work with, and they need to like us. When morale is poor and communication ineffective among members of a treatment team, all suicidal patients are at increased risk. If you are the supervisor, you have a special duty to support your staff, reward them regularly, and see to it that they have what they require to do this difficult work well.

- We whose goal is to save lives should not be actively suicidal ourselves. Because objectivity cannot be maintained when our own problems too closely mirror those of our patients, we should never offer to treat someone who is suicidal if we have been contemplating our own death. Presuming to help others under such circumstances is unethical. If you've been thinking about suicide yourself—which is not rare among therapists—take yourself off any case in which suicide is an issue and get some help.

- If you are the survivor of a suicide yourself—parent, brother, sister, close friend, lover, husband, wife, child—please talk this over with a therapist. Sharing your feelings about this tragedy with a colleague or a suicide survivor group can help, but the objectivity and the structure of a professional therapy arrangement is often best. If you can find a therapist with some specialization in suicide survivor issues, so much the better. Both the American Association of Suicidology (www.suicidology.org) and the American Foundation for Suicide Prevention (www.afsp.org) are good sources for locating support groups and possibly even a specialist in your area. If we are to help suicidal people, we need to take special care to heal ourselves so that we can become strong in the broken places. (I like this image because it comes from Ernest Hemingway, who killed himself.)

- Similarly, if you have ever lost a client to suicide, please seek consultation, support, and, if need be, therapy. Losing a patient to suicide is terribly painful, regardless of whether the therapist is still in training (Knox et al. 2006) or is a senior clinician. I have seen far too many talented and caring people withdraw from their chosen field following the suicide of a patient. Don't let this happen to you.

The most effective therapist for a suicidal patient is someone who has a firm sense of self, a clearly articulated philosophy of life, and the courage to accompany the patient on what is bound to be a sometimes frightening journey. Never losing sight of the fact that our patient's life may be at stake, we must accept this possibility and yet be willing to push ahead into the darkest corners of human experience, where the real work of healing takes place.

Losing a Patient

As I have explained, those of us who work with suicidal people must remember that we, too, need care and support. Whether as suicide interventionists, crisis workers, case managers, or therapists, we're not much good to anyone unless we are in good spirits and getting enough rest. Nor are we of much use unless we're still active in the field of human services.

I say "still active" for a reason. Losing a patient to suicide can be a career-ending experience. Not surprisingly, suicide threats and actual suicide attempts on the part of their patients are two of the most extreme sources of stress that therapists and counselors encounter in their professional work. The death of a patient by suicide is even more traumatic. There is nothing like a completed suicide to devastate our self-esteem and threaten our ability to work successfully with other patients. Therefore, as far as it is possible, we must try to protect ourselves from the tragedy of losing someone to suicide.

We can do so by taking every reasonable step to be sure that a suicidal patient will be safe once he or she leaves our office and that what we understand to be our duties have been carried out to the best of our ability. We take care of ourselves by knowing that we did what any responsible and prudent person with similar training and experience would have done with a similar patient under similar circumstances.

To do our best, all of us can begin by educating ourselves about suicidal behavior and its etiology, including the psychological and medical conditions that contribute to risk, and about the treatment options available to us and how to employ these therapeutic interventions to reduce risk factors and enhance protective factors. This means getting appropriate training and keeping up with developments in research and current best practices.

Suicide in clinical settings is rarely the result of malice or gross neglect on the part of clinicians. But it can be the consequence of core ignorance about suicidal behavior, inadequate assessments of risk, and poor communications among clinical providers or between those providers and a patient's family members, whose vital observations too often go unsought.

It can also be the product of arrogance. If we as clinicians allow ourselves to become so self-assured, so cocky, and so impressed with our own credentials that we cannot even imagine that one of our patients could die by suicide, more of them surely will. Difficult though it may be, if we are to be wise, we must be willing to admit that we don't know everything. We need to remain humble. Obviously, the loss of a patient to suicide is something we all seek to avoid. However, no matter how skilled we are in the treatment of suicidal persons, we may not be able to prevent the suicide of someone in our care.

We also need to understand that our beliefs matter. I

have heard seasoned clinicians remark after a patient's suicide, "Once they make their mind up, there's nothing you can do." Or, "You can't predict this sort of thing, so you can't prevent it, so why try?" Or, "There was no stopping her . . . I finally just gave up." These after-the-fact expressions of futility mirror a suicidal patient's own attitude of hopelessness. While therapists who voice such sentiments cannot reasonably be held accountable for a patient's suicide, their attitude may well have contributed to the eventual outcome.

For that reason, anyone who harbors beliefs such as these—anyone who would argue that suicide is fated and cannot be deterred, anyone who is convinced that there's little point in trying to save someone who is determined to die—has no business working with suicidal people. As professionals, we cannot risk placing a suicidal patient in the care of someone whose attitudes might endanger the person's hope of recovery. Even though we cannot easily afford to lose a single healer who counsels suicidal people, neither can we afford to lose a single patient because the healer was pessimistic about the patient's potential for survival.

The Perils of Denial

Apart from fatalism, one other sure way to increase risk for potentially suicidal people is to dismiss or minimize their talk of suicide and their nonfatal attempts. A poster once distributed by the American Foundation for Suicide Prevention issued a clear warning: "Today's suicide attempter could be tomorrow's suicide." And yet I have conducted at least a dozen death reviews and psychological autopsies of people in whose medical record someone had written (sometimes more than once): "Appears to be manipulating."

This is not to say that suicidal people don't sometimes use the language of suicide in order to manipulate others. As we have seen, they do. For the chronically suicidal, threats of suicide, along with nonfatal attempts, have become a standard coping mechanism. Even someone who is not chronically suicidal may threaten suicide in an attempt to control a loved one or get out of a difficult situation. An angry teenager may threaten to kill himself in order to avoid being expelled from school. Prison inmates may talk of suicide in hopes of being sent to a psychiatric hospital, where the company is apt to be more interesting and they will have a little more freedom.

Of course, some people do more than just talk about suicide: They repeatedly attempt suicide, but in ways that seem destined to fail. This pattern has prompted some researchers to wonder how truly serious such people are about ending their lives. How do these people differ, psychologically, from those who succeed in killing themselves on the very first attempt? And what about people who seem to talk about suicide all the time and yet never actually make an attempt—or those who repeatedly inflict injuries on themselves, and yet the injuries in question have almost no chance of being fatal? Such behavior demands attention, but are these people really in danger of dying?

There are no easy answers to such questions. What is required is a thorough assessment of each individual and the circumstances surrounding the crisis. One thing is clear, however. If a person uses the word *suicide*, even in a statement that appears intended primarily to influence the behavior of others, the possibility of self-inflicted violence has at least been considered. No matter what the situation, an evaluation is always in order.

Substantial research exists to confirm that people who talk about suicide run a higher risk of attempting suicide, and those who attempt suicide are at a higher risk of eventually dying by suicide. In a five-year follow-up study of a group of individuals who had made an attempt on their life, researchers discovered that one-sixth of the group had since died, either of what was unambiguously suicide or as the result of engaging in high-risk behavior of some sort (Rosen 1976; see also Tuckman, Youngman, and Kreizman 1968). A previous suicide attempt is, in fact, the single most powerful predictor of an eventual death by suicide. Experts therefore advise us to take every suicide attempt seriously—and we should.

Nor should talk of suicide ever be taken lightly, even in the absence of openly suicidal behavior. Lest we wind up with another death that could have been prevented, people who threaten suicide must always be carefully assessed by a competent professional, someone who can determine the appropriate course of action. Emerging standards of care require that healthcare professionals and counselors be trained to assess suicide risk and, in particular, to evaluate the likelihood that a suicide threat will be carried out. If we are lucky, a cry for help will not go unheeded but will lead to intervention and treatment that will ultimately result in a healthier, happier person.

The Power of Hope

It is my firm conviction that preventing suicide is fundamentally about the restoration of hope in the hopeless. But if the hopelessness that breeds suicidal thoughts, feelings, and actions is contagious, so, too, is hope. Above all else, we who work with suicidal patients must understand that, even though the patient may wish to give up, we never can. Many of my former patients have told me, years after our work together was completed, that it was my faith in them and in their ultimate victory over despair that kept them going—that kept the spark of hope alive. And I doubt I am alone in this experience. Jerome Groopman's wonderful book *The Anatomy of Hope: How People Prevail in the Face of Illness* offers eloquent testimony to the power of hope in medical settings. Caring treatment and unyielding hope are, indeed, the first and best antidotes to suicide.

Despite the emotional demands of the work, I am chronically optimistic about suicidal people. I believe that a suicide crisis is a terrible thing to waste. A suicide crisis screams out for change, for a re-evaluation of one's life choices, one's relationships, and one's mental and physical habits. A suicide crisis opens fresh opportunities to explore the array of possibilities that life has to offer. In the final analysis, this is perhaps the greatest reward for those of us who work in suicide prevention. Given competent and compassionate care, not merely can suicidal people save themselves from self-destruction, but they can go on from their destination of despair to lead rich and productive lives.

As healers, we must always remember that suicide does not aim to solve extraordinary problems—only ordinary ones that have been magnified beyond their importance by searing psychic pain wrongly believed to be at once unbearable and inescapable. Framing the problem in this way allows our interventions, our gentle yet thought-provoking questions, promptings, and observations, to express what is at once ancient, empathic, tolerant, and kind—our shared humanity. And to the extent that our work reflects this understanding, it is that much more effective.

Suicide does not offer an answer; it poses a question, the answer to which may be a life full of purpose and passion and unencumbered by the fear of tomorrow. If we who counsel suicidal people are unswerving in our belief that suicide can be prevented and that recovery is possible, we can do more than save lives: We can turn them around.

And so, above all, I ask of you this one thing. Think deeply about this good work you have chosen to do. Think of yourself not only as a healer armed with knowledge and skills but as a merchant of hope.

APPENDIX A:
A Sample Protocol

FOR THOSE WHO ARE INTERESTED in further training in the assessment and management of suicide risk, let me briefly review *The QPRT Suicide Risk Management Inventory* (Quinnett and Bratcher 1998). The QPRT (for "Question, Persuade, Refer, or Treat") is a guided clinical interview designed to elicit a narrative report by the suicidal person that will provide a description of the problem(s) suicide would solve and of the events that precipitated the current crisis, as well as information regarding previous instances of suicidal behaviors, family and relationship dynamics, and other known risk and protective factors. The interview also includes a section on securing a commitment from the patient to remain safe and to abide by medical advice and so can be used to generate a shared risk management plan. In addition to the adult outpatient version, inpatient and pediatric versions of the protocol are available (Quinnett, Cardell, and Bratcher 1999; Quinnett and Sowers 1999). The inpatient version is designed to facilitate clinical decisions regarding the appropriate level of monitoring and other risk management practices.

The key clinical questions of the QPRT protocol were developed on the basis of a national survey of experts in suicidology. The authors of the protocol distilled the results into fifteen questions that would yield a standardized and highly effective clinical interview. The pediatric version of the QPRT was based on input from a number of highly regarded child psychologists and child psychiatrists.

As an example of how the protocol works, let us look at the first five questions from the Adult/Older Adult QPRT. The questions are asked after the therapist has established an initial rapport with the patient, and the patient has admitted to suicidal thoughts or feelings or to a suicide attempt, whether recent or remote.

> *What is wrong?* This question clarifies the patient's version of the problem (the only one that really matters).
> *Why now?* This question elicits information about the events that led up to the present suicide crisis.
> *With what?* This question seeks to discover the intended method of suicide and whether the means are readily available to the person.
> *Where and when?* This question reveals the degree of planning and helps the interviewer to determine whether the attempt would in all likelihood be fatal.
> *When and with what in the past?* This question gathers information about past suicide attempts or episodes of serious suicidal thoughts or high-risk behavior.

The interviewer uses these stem questions to frame his or her own queries and records the patient's replies. Answers to these and the remaining ten questions allow an interviewer to perform an appropriately detailed risk assessment and to gain the patient's cooperation in a standard risk management plan, including a safety agreement, consent to a referral, or commitment to participate in treatment.

Competent use of the QPRT protocol requires training. The protocol is currently in use in more than 150 hospitals, mental health centers, and substance abuse treatment facilities nationwide. It has been listed as an example of best practices by the Center for Substance Abuse Treatment at the Department of Health and Human Services and positively reviewed by the Joint Commission (U.S. Department of Health and Human Services 2005; Joint Commission 1999). In 2005, the training program and protocol were adopted for statewide implementation by the mental health leadership in the state of Georgia, with the goal of reducing suicidal behavior among consumers of mental health services.

APPENDIX B:
Suicide Prevention Support System

A VITAL STEP in providing good suicide prevention care is to have the key community support resources already identified and the names of contact persons and their phone numbers readily available. Especially in a crisis situation, you do not want to have to scramble around to find them. Spend the time now to collect this information.

In an emergency:

Ambulance/police: 911

National crisis lines: 1-800-SUICIDE or 1-800-273-TALK

Local crisis line:_____

Crisis response/outreach:_____

In-house security: *(phone)*_____

Nearest emergency room(s):

*(hospital and phone)*_____

*(hospital and phone)*_____

Poison control center:_____

Immediate supervisor: *(name)*_____

*(office phone)*_____ *(home phone)*_____

Contact person/agency for involuntary commitment:

Local mental health numbers:

Agency: _____

Phone: _____

Agency: _____

Phone: _____

Agency: _____

Phone: _____

Mental health specialists who treat suicidal persons:

Name: _____

Phone: _____

Name: _____

Phone: _____

Name: _____

Phone: _____

Child and adolescent specialist: _____

Geriatric mental health specialist: _____

Family therapist: _____

Drug and alcohol specialist: _____

Interpreters: _____

Suicide survivors' group: _____

Additional resources:

_____

_____

_____

FOR FURTHER READING

American Association of Suicidology. 2007. "U.S.A. Suicide: 2005 Official Final Data." Available at http://www.suicidology.org/associations/1045/files/2 005datapgs.pdf

Baumeister, R. F., and M. R. Leary. 1995. "The Need to Belong: Desire for Interpersonal Attachments as a Fundamental Human Motivation." *Psychological Bulletin* 117: 497–529.

Beck, A. T., G. K. Brown, and R. A. Steer. 1997. "Psychometric Characteristics of the Scale for Suicide Ideation with Psychiatric Outpatients." *Behavioral Research and Therapy* 345: 1039–46.

———, G. K. Brown, R. J. Berchick, B. L. Stewart, and R. A. Steer. 1990. "Relationship Between Hopelessness and Ultimate Suicide: A Replication with Psychiatric Outpatients." *American Journal of Psychiatry* 147: 190–95. Reprinted in *Focus* 4, no. 2 (April 2006): 291–96.

———, N. Epstein, G. K. Brown, and R. A. Steer. 1988. "An Inventory for Measuring Clinical Anxiety: Psychometric Properties. *Journal of Consulting and Clinical Psychology* 56, no. 6: 893–97.

———, M. Kovacs, and A. Weissman. 1975. "Hopelessness and Suicidal Behavior: An Overview." *Journal of the American Medical Association* 234, no. 11 (December): 1146–49.

———, R. A. Steer, M. Kovacs, and B. Garrison. 1985. "Hopelessness and Eventual Suicide: A 10-Year

Prospective Study of Patients Hospitalized with Suicidal Ideation." *American Journal of Psychiatry* 142: 559–63.

——, R. A. Steer, and M. G. McElroy. 1982. "Relationships of Hopelessness, Depression, and Previous Suicide Attempts to Suicidal Ideation in Alcoholics." *Journal of Studies on Alcohol* 43: 1042–46.

Bertolote, J. M., A. Fleischmann, D. De Leo, and D. Wasserman. 2004. "Psychiatric Diagnosis and Suicide: Revisiting the Evidence." *Crisis* 25, no. 4: 147–55.

Brown, G. K., T. T. Have, G. R. Henriques, S. X. Xie, J. E. Hollander, and A. T. Beck. 2005. "Cognitive Therapy for the Prevention of Suicide Attempts: A Randomized Controlled Trial. *Journal of the American Medical Association* 294, no. 5 (August): 563–70.

Busch, K. A., J. Fawcett, and D. G. Jacobs. 2003. "Clinical Correlates of Inpatient Suicide." *Journal of Clinical Psychiatry* 64, no. 1: 14–19.

Cobain, Bev. 1998. *When Nothing Matters Anymore: A Survival Guide for Depressed Teens*. Minneapolis: Free Spirit Publishing.

Diagnostic and Statistical Manual of Mental Disorders (DSM-IV-TR). 2000. Fourth edition. Text revision. Arlington, VA: American Psychiatric Association.

Eaton, D. K., L. Kann, S. Kinchen, J. Ross, J. Hawkins, W. A. Harris, R. Lowry, T. McManus, D. Chyen, S. Shanklin, C. Lim, J. A. Grunbaum, and H. Wechsler. 2006. "Youth Risk Behavior Surveillance—United States, 2005." *Morbidity and Mortality Weekly Report: Surveillance Summaries*, vol. 55, no. SS-5 (June 9).

Ellis, Albert, and Catharine MacLaren. 2005. *Rational Emotive Behavior Therapy: A Therapist's Guide*. 2nd edition, revised. Atascadero, CA: Impact Publishers. Originally published 1998.

Ellis, Thomas E., and Cory F. Newman. 1996. *Choosing to Live: How to Defeat Suicide Through Cognitive Therapy*. Oakland, CA: New Harbinger Publications.

Ewing, J.A. 1984. "Detecting Alcoholism: The CAGE Questionnaire." *Journal of the American Medical Association* 252: 1905–7.

Fassler, David G., and Lynne S, Dumas. 1997. *"Help Me, I'm Sad": Recognizing, Treating, and Preventing Childhood and Adolescent Depression.* New York: Penguin.

Fawcett, J. 1997. "Inpatient Management of Suicide." Paper presented at the Harvard Medical School conference Suicide: Critical Issues in Assessment and Management.

———, W. A. Scheftner, L. Fogg, D. C. Clark, M. A. Young, D. Hedeker, and R. Gibbons. 1990. "Time-related Predictors of Suicide in Major Affective Disorders." *American Journal of Psychiatry* 147: 1189–94.

Foster, T. 2001. "Dying for a Drink: Global Suicide Prevention Should Focus More on Alcohol Use Disorders." *British Medical Journal* 323(7317) (October 13): 817–18.

Goldsmith, S. K., T. C. Pellmar, A. M. Kleinman, and W. E. Bunney, eds. 2002. *Reducing Suicide: A National Imperative.* Committee on Pathophysiology and Prevention of Adolescent and Adult Suicide, Board of Neuroscience and Behavioral Health, Institute of Medicine. Washington, D. C.: National Academies Press.

Gould, M. S., F. A. Marrocco, M. Kleinman, J. G. Thomas, K. Mostkoff, J. Cole, and M. Davies. 2005. "Evaluating Iatrogenic Risk of Youth Suicide Screening Programs: A Randomized Controlled Trial." *Journal of the American Medical Association* 293: 1635–43.

Groopman, Jerome. 2003. *The Anatomy of Hope: How People Prevail in the Face of Illness.* New York: Random House.

Hibbeln, J. R. 1998. "Fish Consumption and Major Depression." *Lancet* 351(9110) (April 18): 1213.

Hirayama, T. 1990. *Life-Style and Mortality: A Large-Scale Census-Based Cohort Study in Japan.* Basel: Karger.

Humphry, Derek. 2002. *Final Exit: The Practicalities of Self-Deliverance and Assisted Suicide for the Dying.* Third edition. New York: BantamDell. Originally published 1991.

Hypericum Depression Trial Study Group. 2002. "Effect of *Hypericum perforatum* (St. John's Wort) in Major Depressive Disorder: A Randomized, Controlled Trial." *Journal of the American Medical Association* 287: 1807–14.

Jamison, Kay Redfield. 1999. *Night Falls Fast: Understanding Suicide.* New York: Alfred A. Knopf. Repr. New York: Vintage Books, 2000.

Joiner, T. E., Jr., R. A. Steer, G. Brown, A. T. Beck, J. W. Pettit, and M. D. Rudd. 2003. "Worst-point Suicidal Plans: A Dimension of Suicidality Predictive of Past Suicide Attempts and Eventual Death by Suicide." *Behavioral Research and Therapy* 41, no. 12: 1469–80.

———, M. D. Rudd, and M. H. Rajab. 1997. "The Modified Scale for Suicidal Ideation Among Suicidal Adults: Factors of Suicidality and Their Relation to Clinical and Diagnostic Indicators." *Journal of Abnormal Psychology* 106, no. 2: 260–65.

Joiner, Thomas. 2005. *Why People Die by Suicide.* Cambridge, MA: Harvard University Press.

Joint Commission. 1999. "Asking the 'Suicide Question': Assess Thoroughly and Often to Reduce Risk." *Benchmark* 1, no. 6 (August): 1–3.

———. 2007. "National Patient Safety Goals." Available at http://www.jointcommission.org/PatientSafety/NationalPatientSafetyGoals/07_npsgs.htm

Karch, D., A. Crosby, and T. Simon. 2006. "Toxicology Testing and Results for Suicide Victims—13 States, 2004." *Morbidity and Mortality Weekly Report* 55, no. 46: 1245–48. Reprinted without tables in *Journal of the American Medical Association* 297, no. 4 (January 2007): 355–56.

Knox, S., A. W. Burkard, J. A. Jackson, A. M. Schaack, and S. A. Hess. 2006. "Therapists-in-Training Who Experience a Client Suicide: Implications for Supervision." *Professional Psychology: Research and Practice* 37, no. 5: 547–57.

Linehan, M. M. 1993a. *Cognitive-Behavioral Treatment of Borderline Personality Disorder*. New York: Guilford Press.

———. 1993b. *Skills Training Manual for Treating Borderline Personality Disorder*. New York: Guilford Press.

———. 1999. "Standard Protocol for Assessing and Treating Suicidal Behaviors for Patients in Treatment." In Douglas G. Jacobs, ed., *The Harvard Medical School Guide to Suicide Assessment and Intervention*, pp. 146–87. San Francisco: Jossey-Bass.

———, H. E. Armstrong, A. Suarez, D. Allmon, and H. L. Heard. 1991. "Cognitive-Behavioral Treatment of Chronically Parasuicidal Borderline Patients." *Archives of General Psychiatry* 48, no. 12: 1060–64.

Marzuk, P. M., K. Tardiff, A. C. Leon, C. S. Hirsch, L. Portera, N. Hartwell, and M. I. Iqbal. 1997. "Lower Risk of Suicide During Pregnancy." *American Journal of Psychiatry* 154, no. 1: 122–23.

Menninger, Karl. 1938. *Man Against Himself*. New York: Harcourt, Brace & World. Repr. New York: Harcourt Brace Jovanovich, 1985.

Murphy, G. E., and R. D. Wetzel. 1990. "The Lifetime Risk of Suicide in Alcoholism." *Archives of General Psychiatry* 47, no. 4: 383–92.

Nemets, H., B. Nemets, A. Apater, Z. Bracha, and R. H. Belmaker. 2006. "Omega-3 Treatment of Childhood Depression: A Controlled, Double-blind Pilot Study." *American Journal of Psychiatry* 163, no. 6: 1098–100.

Palmer, B. A., V. S. Pankratz, and J. M. Bostwick. 2005. "The Lifetime Risk of Suicide in Schizophrenia: A Reexamination." *Archives of General Psychiatry* 62: 247–53.

Parker, G., N. A. Gibson, H. Brotchie, G. Heruc, A. M. Rees, and D. Hadzi-Pavlovic. 2006. "Omega-3 Fatty Acids and Mood Disorders." *American Journal of Psychiatry* 163, no. 6: 969–78.

Petronis, K. R., J. F. Samuels, E. K. Moscicki, and J. C. Anthony. 1990. "An Epidemiologic Investigation of

Potential Risk Factors for Suicide Attempts." *Social Psychiatry and Psychiatric Epidemiology* 25, no. 4: 193–99.

Quinnett, Paul G. 1998. "Consumer Response to a Suicide Risk Assessment Interview." Paper presented at the annual meeting of the American Association of Suicidology, Houston, Texas (April).

———. 1992. *Suicide: The Forever Decision—For Those Thinking About Suicide, and For Those Who Know, Love, or Counsel Them.* Revised edition. New York: Crossroad Publishing. Available at http://www.qprinstitute.com/Foreverweb.htm

———, and Kevin Bratcher. 1998. *The QPRT Suicide Risk Management Inventory—Adult/Older Adult Version.* Spokane, WA: QPR Institute, Inc.

———, Rebecca Cardell, and Kevin Bratcher. 1999. *The QPRT Suicide Risk Management Inventory—Hospital Version.* Spokane, WA: QPR Institute, Inc.

———, and Louis Sowers. 1999. *The QPRT Suicide Risk Management Inventory—Pediatric Version.* Spokane, WA: QPR Institute, Inc.

Rosen, D. H. 1976. "The Serious Suicide Attempt: Five-year Follow-up Study of 886 Patients." *Journal of the American Medical Association* 235, no. 19: 2105–9.

Rudd, M. D., A. L. Berman, T. E. Joiner Jr., M. K. Nock, M. M. Silverman, M. Mandrusiak, K. A. Van Orden, and T. Witte. 2006. "Warning Signs for Suicide: Theory, Research, and Clinical Applications." *Suicide and Life-threatening Behavior* 36, no. 3: 255–62.

———, T. E. Joiner Jr., and M. H. Rajab. 1996. "Relationships Among Suicide Ideators, Attempters, and Multiple Attempters in a Young-Adult Sample." *Journal of Abnormal Psychology* 105, no. 4: 541–50.

Shenk, Joshua Wolf. 2005. *Lincoln's Melancholy: How Depression Challenged a President and Fueled His Greatness.* New York: Houghton Mifflin.

Shneidman, E. S. 1998. "Perspectives on Suicidology: Further Reflections on Suicide and Psychache." *Suicide* and *Life-threatening Behavior* 28, no. 3: 245–50.

Simon, G. E., J. Savarino, B. Operskalski, and P. S. Wang. 2006. "Suicide Risk During Antidepressant Treatment." *American Journal of Psychiatry* 163: 41–47.

Simon, R. I., and D. W. Shuman. 2006. "The Standard of Care in Suicide Risk Assessment: An Elusive Concept." *CNS Spectrums* 11, no. 6: 442–45.

Slaby, Andrew, and Lili Frank Garfinkel. 1994. *No One Saw My Pain: Why Teens Kill Themselves*. New York: W. W. Norton.

Slovenko, R. 2002. *Law in Psychiatry*. New York: Brunner-Routledge.

Stoll, A. L. *The Omega-3 Connection*. New York: Simon & Schuster, 2001.

——, W. E. Severus, M. P. Freeman, S. Rueter, H. A. Zboyan, E. Diamond, K. K. Cress, and L. B. Marangell. 1999. "Omega 3 Fatty Acids in Bipolar Disorder: A Preliminary Double-blind, Placebo-Controlled Trial." *Archives of General Psychiatry* 56, no. 5 (May): 407–12.

Strosahl, K., J. A. Chiles, and M. M. Linehan. 1992. "Prediction of Suicide Intent in Hospitalized Parasuicides: Reasons for Living, Hopelessness, and Depression." *Comprehensive Psychiatry* 36, no. 6: 366–73.

Styron, William. 1990. *Darkness Visible: A Memoir of Madness*. New York: Random House; repr. New York: Vintage Books, 1992.

Tondo, L., and R. J. Baldessarini. 2003. "Suicide Risk and Treatment for Patients with Bipolar Disorder." *Journal of the American Medical Association* 290: 1517–19.

Tuckman, J., W. F. Youngman, and G. Kreizman. 1968. "Multiple Suicide Attempts." *Community Mental Health Journal* 4, no. 2: 164–70.

U.S. Department of Health and Human Services. 1996. *Physical Activity and Health: A Report of the Surgeon General*. Atlanta: U.S. Department of Health and Human Services, Centers for Disease Control and Prevention, National Center for Chronic Disease Prevention and Health Promotion. Available online at http://www.cdc.gov/nccdphp/sgr/mm.htm

———. 2005. *Treatment Improvement Protocol Series No. 42: Substance Abuse Treatment for Persons with Co-Occurring Disorders.* DHHS publication no. (SMA) 05-3922. Rockville, MD: Substance Abuse and Mental Health Services Administration, Center for Substance Abuse Treatment.

U. S. Public Health Service. 1999. *The Surgeon General's Call to Action to Prevent Suicide.* Washington, D.C.: U. S. Department of Health and Human Services.

Weissman, A. D., A. T. Beck, and J. Kovacs. 1979. "Drug Abuse, Hopelessness, and Suicidal Behavior." *International Journal of Addiction* 14: 451–62.

Williams, J.M.G., T. Barnhofer, C. Crane, and A. T. Beck. 2005. "Problem Solving Deteriorates Following Mood Challenge in Formerly Depressed Patients with a History of Suicidal Ideation." *Journal of Abnormal Psychology* 114, no. 3 (August): 421–31.

———, D. S. Duggan, C. Crane, and M.J.V. Fennell. 2006. "Mindfulness-based Cognitive Therapy for Prevention or Recurrence of Suicidal Behavior." *Journal of Clinical Psychology: In Session* 62, no. 2: 201–10.